coke

OR

pepsi?

FOREVER!

What do you really know about your friends?

C or P

SCHOLASTIC INC.

New York Toronto London Auckland Sydney Mexico City New Delhi Hong Kong

coke
OR
pepsi?

FOREVER!

Written and designed by
Mickey & Cheryl Gill

ISBN 978-0-545-48592-0

12 11 10 9 8 7 6 5 4 3 2 1   12 13 14 15 16 17/0

Printed in China   53

First Scholastic printing, September 2012

Pass this book around to all your friends.
Each friend has a chance to answer
some pretty cool questions.

See what you
have in common.

Find out what makes you
different.

Some answers might
shock you.

If you love
this book,
check out these
other
coke or pepsi?
books!

Please pass
this book back to

Alexa H.

Name

_____ makes me laugh hard.

Favorite thing that comes in a bag?

⬤ Castle in the mountains
◯ Cottage in the woods

Birthday (Nov 13 2008)

City you were born in?

◯ Moonlight   ⬤ Sunshine

Coolest animal with whiskers?

1. Name (Alexa)

2. ○ Cinnamon ● Fruity ○ Minty gum?

3. What do you love about yourself? ___I'm___ =sporty___

4. Where were you last time you used mustard? _____

5. The last paper I wrote for a class was about _____

_____ .

6. I could never eat _____ again and be OK.

7. TV show you most belong on? _____

8. WOULD YOU RATHER BE THE ○ STAR ON A LOSING TEAM ○ WORST ON A STAR TEAM?

9. Ever carved anything in a tree? ○ Yes ○ No

10. ● Swim with the dolphins ○ Pet a manatee?

11. Would you rather be a ○ giant ● pixie?

12. ● Fuzzy socks ○ Warm slippers?

13. Hot chocolate ○ with ○ without marshmallows?

14. Good at sneaking up on people? ○ Not really ○ Kind of ○ Absolutely!

15. Scariest thing you've done on purpose? _____

16. New pair of ○ jeans ○ shoes?

17. If I could _____, I would be thrilled.

18. Age you turned on fave birthday? ( )

19. Something you would love to see? _____

20. Which is worse? ○ Really sad ○ Out-of-control mad

○ Potato chips
○ French fries?

○ Fashionable
○ Casual?

○ Brownies
○ Chocolate chip cookies?

○ Sunset
○ Sunrise?

coke OR *pepsi?*

classic

Best holiday? (   )

Fave actor? (   )

Fave actress?
(   )

One word to
describe you?
(   )

○ Big Mac
○ Whopper?

○ Gold
○ Silver?

coke-or-pepsi.com

1. Name _____

2. ◯ Skinny jeans ◯ Jeggings ◯ Neither?

3. Happiest color? _____

4. What were you doing in the last photo taken of you? _____

5. Where were you? _____

6. **Know how to cook?** ◯ **No** ◯ **A little** ◯ **Yes**

7. If yes to #6, what's your specialty? _____

8. Are you usually ◯ cold ◯ hot?

9. Famous person you admire most? _____

10. DO HORROR MOVIES FRIGHTEN YOU? ◯ **NOT REALLY** ◯ **YES, NIGHTMARES!**

11. Fave outfit to relax in? _____

12. Ever shoot a spitball? ◯ Yes ◯ Gross, no!

13. Favorite thing that comes in your mail? _____.

14. Sprinkles ◯ always make me happy ◯ are kinda overrated.

15. Any phobias or fears? ◯ Nope ◯ Yes, I'm afraid of _____.

16. ◯ Drama queen ◯ Cool, calm, and collected?

17. What do you crave? _____

18. Drink after other people? ◯ Yeah ◯ Sometimes ◯ Never! Germs!

19. Ever encountered a bat? ◯ Yes ◯ No

20. What do you hear right now? _____

Ahh! You're going to wear that?

Scare-crow! Caww!

1. Name

2. Afraid to cross bridges? ○ Yes ○ No

3. Can you wiggle your ears without using your hands? ○ No ○ Yes

4. Do you ○ give in ○ get your way?

5. LAST THING YOU SOLD FOR YOUR SCHOOL? _____

6. Go to the library? ○ No ○ Yes

7. Longest word you know? _____

8. Can you hang a spoon from your nose? ○ Yes ○ No ○ Huh?

9. Best food with a glass of milk? _____

10. Gold ○ fish ○ bracelet?

11. **Any strange talent?** ○ No ○ Yes, I _____.

12. Spend the night in a haunted house? ○ NO! ○ Sure, I don't believe.

13. It's scary how much I like _____.

14. Give good manicures? ○ Yes ○ No

15. Favorite reality show? _____

16. Scrambled eggs are ○ yummy ○ frightening.

17. Worst thing about your brother(s)/sister(s)? _____

18. Best thing about your brother(s)/sister(s)? _____

19. LOVE A GOOD MYSTERY? ○ YES! ○ NAH

20. Think you're creative? ○ Yes ○ A little ○ Not really

Name

1. swim with a huge, harmless whale in the ocean, would you? ○ Yes ○ No, but I would swim with _____.

2. slow down time, which event would you slow down? _____

3. add sisters or brothers to your family, which genders and ages would you choose?

_____

4. have absolutely anything for dinner tonight, what would you pick? _____

_____

5. do one fun thing with an alien visiting our planet, what would it be? _____

_____

6. become any object for just one day, what would you be? Why? _____

_____

7. be an exchange student for one year anywhere in the world, which country would you visit? _____

8. be great friends with someone from the past, who would you choose? Why?

_____

9. do absolutely anything for just one year, what would you do? _____

_____

10. change your last name, without hurting your parents' feelings, would you?

○ No ○ Yes, I would change it to _____.

coke-or-pepsi.com

First thing that comes to mind when you see or hear these words?

(another word, sentence, or super short story)

Name

1. Corn on the cob . . . .
2. Dark alley . . . .
3. Roller coaster . . . .
4. Pigs in blankets . . . .
5. Hamster . . . .
6. Pink . . . .
7. Glow-in-the-dark . . . .
8. The letter U . . . .
9. Hello Kitty . . . .
10. Face painting . . . .
11. Super star . . . .
12. Bell . . . .
13. Sleeping bag . . . .
14. Hollywood . . . .
15. Rock . . . .
16. Piano . . . .
17. Magazine . . . .
18. Watermelon . . . .
19. Bubbles . . . .
20. Subway . . . .

classic

- ⊙ Waffle cone
- ⊙ Sugar cone
- ⊙ Cup?

- ⊙ Ice cubes
- ⊙ Crushed ice?

- ⊙ TV
- ⊙ Book?

- ⊙ Beach
- ⊙ Mountains?

- ⊙ Go with the flow
- ⊙ Stick to a routine?

- ⊙ Ice cream
- ⊙ Fro-yo?

Favorite relative?

Best amusement park ride?

Favorite game?

Best book?

last things i painted were my nails

1. Name (_____)

2. Best thing in a spray can? ○ **Whipped Cream** ○ **Cheese Whiz** ○ **Paint**

3. Ever sprayed whipped cream directly in your mouth? ○ Yes ○ No

4. Last thing you painted? _____

5. Last thing you had stuck in your hair? _____

6. ○ Donuts ○ Donut holes

7. Worse T-shirt color? ○ **Orange** ○ **Yellow** ○ **Green**

8. What are you a beginner at? _____

9. What are you an expert at? _____

10. Favorite dip? _____

11. Favorite thing to dip? _____

12. Scarves? ○ Luv 'em ○ Hate 'em, so restricting!

13. I heart _____.

14. _____ is epic.

15. Friend with the coolest family? _____

16. ○ Red velvet cheesecake brownie ○ S'more-stuffed chocolate chip cookie?

17. Fave flave for lipgloss? _____

18. Favorite emoticon? _____

19. ○ Abracadabra ○ Bipiddi-boppidi-boo ○ Expelliarmus?

20. ○ Lemonade ○ Pink Lemonade?

I like movies that make me cry

1. Name
2. Last animated movie you saw?_____
3. Movies ○ with happy endings ○ that leave you thinking?
4. Sleepovers? ○ Fun! ○ Ugh.
5. ○ French Bulldog ○ Irish Setter ○ Alaskan Husky?
6. **Movies** ○ **at the theater** ○ **at home?**
7. Are you a ○ share-your-umbrella ○ every-girl-for-herself kinda girl?
8. ○ Polo ○ Graphic Tee?
9. **Love to see a** ○ **volcano erupt** ○ **total eclipse of the sun?**
10. What does your hair do on rainy days? _____
11. ○ **Write a great novel** ○ **Travel around the world?**
12. ○ Hike through the woods ○ Stroll through the city?
13. Ever danced the hula? ○ Yes ○ No
14. **Very first song you remember liking?**_____
15. Maple syrup on ○ waffles ○ French toast?
16. Ever fallen backwards in a chair? ○ Yes ○ No
17. **Wear shoes in the house?** ○ **Yes** ○ **Sometimes** ○ **Never**
18. If you get married, will you ○ keep ○ ditch ○ combine your last name(s)?
19. ○ Pack light ○ Certified overpacker?
20. FAVE SONG TO SING ON ROCK BAND OR GUITAR HERO?_____

I'll never get rid of my chucks

1. Name ⬚

2. On anyone's bad side right now? ○ Yes ○ No

3. WORN-OUT ITEM YOU CAN'T PART WITH? _____

4. ○ Italian ice ○ French vanilla ice cream ○ German chocolate cake?

5. Most unusual animal you've ever fed? _____

6. When things get hard, do you usually ○ give up ○ keep trying?

7. SCHOOL UNIFORMS? ○ FOR IT ○ AGAINST?

8. ○ Sweater ○ Hoodie?

9. One thing you'd like to learn to do well? _____

10. **Pigs are ○ so cute ○ muddy, stinky, and gross.**

11. Wear glitter? ○ Yes, love the sparkle! ○ Nah, too gaudy.

12. Glow sticks? ○ Still fun ○ Ho hum

13. Last thing you do before you turn off the lights? _____

14. Love ○ notes ○ letter ○ potion?

15. ○ Brownie ○ Girl Scout ○ Other _____ ○ None?

16. Favorite Girl Scout cookie? _____

17. Lucky charm or something lucky you wear? ○ No ○ Yes, _____.

18. Ever run a lemonade stand? ○ Yes ○ No

19. Kind of business you'd like to start someday? _____

20. **I would love to be president of _____.**

Twofers

Name _____

1. **Fave sweet and salty combo?** _____

2. Reasons for being late? _____

3. **Things you always have with you?** _____

4. Fave furry animals? _____

5. **Habits you have?** _____

6. Stuff outside your bedroom window? _____

7. **Places you love?** _____

8. Things you've climbed? _____

9. **Words you really love?** _____

10. Qualities you like in a friend? _____

11. **Things that make you mad?** _____

12. Fave animals that swim in the sea? _____

13. **Green things you'll eat?** _____

14. Black and white things you like? _____

15. **Beverages you drink almost every day?** _____

16. Things you love that fit in your hand? _____

17. **Friends you talk to almost every day?** _____

18. Colors you like to paint your toenails? _____

19. **Stuff you've won?** _____

20. Things you've lost? _____

1 question.
2 answers.

_____ forever.

_____

_____

_____ are so cute!

_____

_____

_____

_____ are awesome words!

_____

_____

_____

_____

_____

_____

_____ are my favorites.

_____

_____ are missing.

1. Name ⬭

2. Leopard prints are so ○ chic ○ tacky?

3. ○ Seven dwarves ○ One fairy godmother?

4. How many tiaras do you own? ⬭

5. Mannequins give you the creeps? ○ No ○ Yes

6. Ever been in a corn maze? ○ Yes ○ No ○ Not sure, what is that?

7. Last school project you did? _____

8. British accents sound ○ so cool ○ smart ○ kinda snobby?

9. ○ Pair of glass slippers ○ Pumpkin that turns into a carriage?

10. Magic ○ potion ○ wand ○ markers?

11. ○ Sand between your toes ○ Out too deep to touch bottom?

12. Bowling? ○ Ridiculous ○ Fun ○ Ridiculously fun!

13. What do you talk about more than anything? _____

14. Would you rather be a ○ princess ○ princess' sister?

15. Skinny jeans with ○ flats ○ flip-flops ○ sneakers?

16. Today are you ○ fairest of them all ○ "sleepy" beauty?

17. Three words to describe your life? _____

18. Favorite song to sing with friends? _____

19. How 'bout to dance to with friends? _____

20. I wish I were a(n) ○ English ○ history ○ math ○ science whiz!

Who's the worst of the fairy tale foes?

○ Wicked queen step-mother

○ Super mean step-sisters

○ Other

_____

_____

classic

○ Coke ○ Pepsi?

○ Hot dog ○ Hamburger?

○ Milk ○ Dark chocolate?

○ Butterflies ○ Dragonflies?

○ Small talk
○ Deep conversation?

○ Sneakers ○ Flip-flops?

Best movie ever? _____

_____

Worst movie ever? _____

_____

Favorite number? Why? _____

_____

○ Reality show ○ Sitcom?

○ Bicycle through Europe
○ African safari?

What scares you? _____

_____

Fave school subject? _____

_____

I LOVE TWISTER!

1. Name ( )

2. Which have you taken a ride on? ○ **Horse** ○ **Elephant** ○ **Camel** ○ **None!**

3. Team(s) you like to root for? _____

4. Favorite pasta topping? ○ Meatballs ○ Cheese ○ Other _____

5. ○ Pencil ○ Pen ○ Keyboard?

6. Own a pair of boots? ○ **No** ○ **Yes,** ( ) **pairs.**

7. How 'bout a cowboy hat? ○ Yep ○ No way

8. Like peanut butter? ○ No ○ Yes, _____ is my favorite kind.

9. Think quiet people are ○ smart ○ shy ○ not interested?

10. Ideal summer vacation? _____

11. Play a mean game of ping pong? ○ Yep, I'm awesome. ○ I'm OK. ○ No!

12. Last time you played Twister? _____

13. ○ Zoo ○ Aquarium ○ Neither, I like animals in the wild.

14. Do you like Scrabble? ○ Yes ○ No

15. Singer/Band that appears the most on your playlists? _____

16. ZOMBIES ARE CHASING YOU. WHO DO YOU WANT WITH YOU? _____

17. Huge sale at the mall. Who would you want with you? _____

18. Tried raw oysters? ○ No ○ Yes   Did you like? ○ No! Ick! ○ Yes

19. Three things for a perfect weekend? _____

20. Own anything with polka dots on it? ○ **Of course** ○ **Nope**

I AM NOT A BRAT!

1. Name (_____)

2. Last thing you put ketchup on? _____

3. ○ Goldfish ○ Hermit crab ○ Iguana ○ Gross! None!

4. **Musical instrument you gave up?** _____

5. ○ Online ○ Phone?

6. How many cousins do you have? (_____)

7. Ever been on YouTube? ○ Yes ○ No

8. If yes, what for? _____

9. **Which is cuter?** ○ **Rabbit** ○ **Guinea pig**

10. Use a calendar? ○ Yes ○ No

11. Coolest thing about your pet? _____

12. Currently ○ in braces ○ wearing a retainer ○ free of devices!

13. **Last flick you cried at?** _____

14. Text/Chat abbreviation you use a lot? _____

15. Are you a brat? ○ No ○ Sometimes ○ Pretty much

16. Sport you gave up? _____

17. Who thinks just like you? _____

18. ○ East Coast ○ West Coast ○ In the Middle?

19. First thing you do when you wake up? _____

20. What do you want to be doing by age 25? _____

Name

Why were you named that?

Do you like it?

→ Yes   No ◼

Fave thing that comes in a wrapper?

Would you rather ...

◼ Swim like a dolphin   ◼ Fly like an eagle?

Can you tie a good bow?

◼ Yes   No ◼

Where would you swim to?   **Where would you fly to?**

Do you interrrupt people?

◼ Yes ☹   ◼ No ☺

◼ Shake   ◼ Malt → **What IS malt?**

Fave flave?

Flower power girl power

1. Name _____

2. How tall are you? _____

3. Super nice to someone this week? ○ Yes ☺ ○ No

4. Most glamorous thing you own? _____

5. Time you wake up on a school day? (_____)

6. Time you wake up on the weekend? (_____)

7. If you could be an Olympian, which sport would you choose? _____

8. Everything tastes better with _____.

9. Ever had dessert for breakfast? ○ Oh yeah ○ Nope

10. ○ Throw away ○ Donate ○ Keep too much?

11. Band you would love to tour with? _____

12. Would you add color stripes to your hair? ○ No ○ Yes ○ Already did!

13. Favorite teacher? _____

14. ○ Relax in a pair of jeans ○ Twirl in a beautiful ball gown?

15. Coconut ○ cream pie ○ cake ○ not a coconut fan

16. Snow ○ cone ○ day ○ sledding?

17. Best party you've gone to? _____

18. Crush know you exist? ○ Yes ○ No ○ Don't have one

19. Where are you in family's birth order? _____

20. When you tell a story, do you ○ exaggerate ○ stick to the facts ○ do both?

PEACE FOREVER

1. Name _____

2. I'm wearing ○ lip gloss ○ nail polish ○ neither.

3. Which is worse? ○ Homework ○ Cleaning your room

4. How many pillows do you sleep with? _____

5. Favorite window to look out? _____

6. Something a parent does that drives you nuts? _____

7. Actress you would love to be a personal assistant to? _____

8. Are you more of a ○ pants ○ skirt girl?

9. If you could change one thing today, what would it be? _____

10. If you were an instrument, what would you be? _____

11. Best part of being a super heroine? ○ Power ○ Costume ○ Cool name

12. If you could only visit 1 Website this month, which would it be? _____

13. Best class trip ever? _____

14. Quality a friend has you wished you had? _____

15. One weird fact you know? _____

16. Coolest thing you've ever found? _____

17. Know anything about family ancestors? ○ No ○ Yes, _____.

18. Fave sleepover snacks? _____

19. Coordinate shoes and bag? ○ Always ○ Sometimes ○ Who cares?

20. If you had a safe, what would you keep in it? _____

If you were ...

Name

1. **a mermaid,** where in the world would you want to live? Why?

_____

2. **President,** what kind of room would you add to the White House?

_____

3. an exotic **animal keeper,** which animals would you want to care for?

_____

4. **in charge** of naming the next kind of American spacecraft, what awesome
name would you give it? _____

5. **a dog,** which neighborhood dogs would you want to hang with? Why?

_____

6. **a teacher,** what cool activity would you do with your class?

_____

7. **in charge of your school** for a day, what would you change?

_____

8. **going to live** on the moon for one year who would you take with you?
Why? _____

9. **able to stay** the same age for the rest of your life, which age would you
pick? Why? _____

10. able to have any **talent** you don't currently have, what would it be?

_____

First thing that comes to mind when you see or hear these words?

(another word, sentence, or super short story)

1. Panda bear . . . .
2. Hysterical . . . .
3. Fireworks . . . .
4. T-shirt . . . .
5. Marshmallow . . . .
6. Celery sticks . . . .
7. Raisins . . . .
8. Poodle . . . .
9. Sunglasses . . . .
10. Chucks . . . .
11. Stick people . . . .
12. Physical Education . . . .
13. Mountain . . . .
14. Scooter . . . .
15. Pyramid . . . .
16. Diamonds . . . .
17. Hot peppers . . . .
18. Ringtone . . . .
19. Nail polish . . . .
20. Alligator . . . .

Name

1. Name ⟨_____⟩

2. ○ Cinnamon ○ Fruity ○ Minty gum?

3. What do you love about yourself? _____

4. Where were you last time you used mustard? _____

5. The last paper I wrote for a class was about _____

_____ .

6. I could never eat _____ again and be OK.

7. TV show you most belong on? _____

8. WOULD YOU RATHER BE THE ○ STAR ON A LOSING TEAM ○ WORST ON A STAR TEAM?

9. Ever carved anything in a tree? ○ Yes ○ No

10. ○ Swim with the dolphins ○ Pet a manatee?

11. Would you rather be a ○ giant ○ pixie?

12. ○ Fuzzy socks ○ Warm slippers?

13. Hot chocolate ○ with ○ without marshmallows?

14. Good at sneaking up on people? ○ Not really ○ Kind of ○ Absolutely!

15. Scariest thing you've done on purpose? _____

16. New pair of ○ jeans ○ shoes?

17. If I could _____ , I would be thrilled.

18. Age you turned on fave birthday? ⟨_____⟩

19. Something you would love to see?_____

20. Which is worse? ○ Really sad ○ Out-of-control mad

○ Potato chips
○ French fries?

coke OR pepsi?

○ Fashionable
○ Casual?

classic

○ Sunset
○ Sunrise?

○ Brownies
○ Chocolate chip cookies?

Best holiday?

Fave actor?

Fave actress?

One word to
describe you?

○ Big Mac
○ Whopper?

○ Gold
○ Silver?

coke-or-pepsi.com

1. Name _____

2. ⭕ Skinny jeans ⭕ Jeggings ⭕ Neither?

3. *Happiest color?* _____

4. **What were you doing in the last photo taken of you?** _____

5. Where were you? _____

6. Know how to cook? ⭕ No ⭕ A little ⭕ Yes

7. If yes to #6, what's your specialty? _____

8. Are you usually ⭕ cold ⭕ hot?

9. Famous person you admire most? _____

10. DO HORROR MOVIES FRIGHTEN YOU? ⭕ NOT REALLY ⭕ YES, NIGHTMARES!

11. Fave outfit to relax in? _____

12. Ever shoot a spitball? ⭕ Yes ⭕ Gross, no!

13. **Favorite thing that comes in your mail?** _____.

14. Sprinkles ⭕ always make me happy ⭕ are kinda overrated.

15. Any phobias or fears? ⭕ Nope ⭕ Yes, I'm afraid of _____.

16. ⭕ Drama queen ⭕ Cool, calm, and collected?

17. What do you crave? _____

18. Drink after other people? ⭕ Yeah ⭕ Sometimes ⭕ Never! Germs!

19. Ever encountered a bat? ⭕ Yes ⭕ No

20. What do you hear right now? _____

Ahh! You're going to wear that?

Scare-crow! Caww!

1. Name

2. Afraid to cross bridges? ⚪ Yes ⚪ No

3. Can you wiggle your ears without using your hands? ⚪ No ⚪ Yes

4. Do you ⚪ give in ⚪ get your way?

5. LAST THING YOU SOLD FOR YOUR SCHOOL? _____

6. Go to the library? ⚪ No ⚪ Yes

7. Longest word you know? _____

8. Can you hang a spoon from your nose? ⚪ Yes ⚪ No ⚪ Huh?

9. Best food with a glass of milk? _____

10. Gold ⚪ fish ⚪ bracelet?

11. Any strange talent? ⚪ No ⚪ Yes, I _____.

12. Spend the night in a haunted house? ⚪ NO! ⚪ Sure, I don't believe.

13. It's scary how much I like _____.

14. Give good manicures? ⚪ Yes ⚪ No

15. Favorite reality show? _____

16. Scrambled eggs are ⚪ yummy ⚪ frightening.

17. Worst thing about your brother(s)/sister(s)? _____

18. Best thing about your brother(s)/sister(s)? _____

19. LOVE A GOOD MYSTERY? ⚪ YES! ⚪ NAH

20. Think you're creative? ⚪ Yes ⚪ A little ⚪ Not really

IF YOU COULD...

Name _____

1. swim with a huge, harmless whale in the ocean, would you? ○ Yes ○ No, but I

   would swim with _____.

2. slow down time, which event would you slow down? _____

3. add sisters or brothers to your family, which genders and ages would you choose?

   _____

4. have absolutely anything for dinner tonight, what would you pick? _____

   _____

5. do one fun thing with an alien visiting our planet, what would it be? _____

   _____

6. become any object for just one day, what would you be? Why? _____

   _____

7. be an exchange student for one year anywhere in the world, which country

   would you visit? _____

8. be great friends with someone from the past, who would you choose? Why?

   _____

9. do absolutely anything for just one year, what would you do? _____

   _____

10. change your last name, without hurting your parents' feelings, would you?

    ○ No ○ Yes, I would change it to _____.

coke-or-pepsi.com

First thing that comes to mind when you see or hear these words?

(another word, sentence, or super short story)

Name

1. Corn on the cob . . . .
2. Dark alley . . . .
3. Roller coaster . . . .
4. Pigs in blankets . . . .
5. Hamster . . . .
6. Pink . . . .
7. Glow-in-the-dark . . . .
8. The letter U . . . .
9. Hello Kitty . . . .
10. Face painting . . . .
11. Super star . . . .
12. Bell . . . .
13. Sleeping bag . . . .
14. Hollywood . . . .
15. Rock . . . .
16. Piano . . . .
17. Magazine . . . .
18. Watermelon . . . .
19. Bubbles . . . .
20. Subway . . . .

classic

- ○ **Waffle cone**
- ○ **Sugar cone**
- ○ **Cup?**

- ○ **Ice cubes**
- ○ **Crushed ice?**

- ○ **TV**
- ○ **Book?**

- ○ **Beach**
- ○ **Mountains?**

- ○ **Go with the flow**
- ○ **Stick to a routine?**

- ○ **Ice cream**
- ○ **Fro-yo?**

Favorite relative?

Best amusement park ride?

Favorite game?

Best book?

last things i painted were my nails

1. Name _____

2. Best thing in a spray can? ○ **Whipped Cream** ○ **Cheese Whiz** ○ **Paint**

3. Ever sprayed whipped cream directly in your mouth? ○ Yes ○ No

4. Last thing you painted? _____

5. Last thing you had stuck in your hair? _____

6. ○ Donuts ○ Donut holes

7. Worse T-shirt color? ○ Orange ○ Yellow ○ Green

8. What are you a beginner at? _____

9. What are you an expert at? _____

10. Favorite dip? _____

11. Favorite thing to dip? _____

12. Scarves? ○ Luv 'em ○ Hate 'em, so restricting!

13. I heart _____.

14. _____ is epic.

15. Friend with the coolest family? _____

16. ○ Red velvet cheesecake brownie ○ S'more-stuffed chocolate chip cookie?

17. Fave flave for lipgloss? _____

18. Favorite emoticon? _____

19. ○ Abracadabra ○ Bipiddi-boppidi-boo ○ Expelliarmus?

20. ○ Lemonade ○ Pink Lemonade?

I like movies that make me cry

1. Name _____

2. Last animated movie you saw? _____

3. Movies ○ with happy endings ○ that leave you thinking?

4. Sleepovers? ○ Fun! ○ Ugh.

5. ○ French Bulldog ○ Irish Setter ○ Alaskan Husky?

6. **Movies** ○ **at the theater** ○ **at home?**

7. Are you a ○ share-your-umbrella ○ every-girl-for-herself kinda girl?

8. ○ Polo ○ Graphic Tee?

9. Love to see a ○ volcano erupt ○ total eclipse of the sun?

10. What does your hair do on rainy days? _____

11. ○ **Write a great novel** ○ **Travel around the world?**

12. ○ Hike through the woods ○ Stroll through the city?

13. Ever danced the hula? ○ Yes ○ No

14. **Very first song you remember liking?** _____

15. Maple syrup on ○ waffles ○ French toast?

16. Ever fallen backwards in a chair? ○ Yes ○ No

17. **Wear shoes in the house?** ○ **Yes** ○ **Sometimes** ○ **Never**

18. If you get married, will you ○ keep ○ ditch ○ combine your last name(s)?

19. ○ Pack light ○ Certified overpacker?

20. FAVE SONG TO SING ON ROCK BAND OR GUITAR HERO? _____

I'll never get rid of my chucks

1. Name
2. On anyone's bad side right now? ○ Yes ○ No
3. WORN-OUT ITEM YOU CAN'T PART WITH? _____
4. ○ Italian ice ○ French vanilla ice cream ○ German chocolate cake?
5. Most unusual animal you've ever fed? _____
6. When things get hard, do you usually ○ give up ○ keep trying?
7. SCHOOL UNIFORMS? ○ FOR IT ○ AGAINST?
8. ○ Sweater ○ Hoodie?
9. One thing you'd like to learn to do well? _____
10. Pigs are ○ so cute ○ muddy, stinky, and gross.
11. Wear glitter? ○ Yes, love the sparkle! ○ Nah, too gaudy.
12. Glow sticks? ○ Still fun ○ Ho hum
13. Last thing you do before you turn off the lights? _____
14. Love ○ notes ○ letter ○ potion?
15. ○ Brownie ○ Girl Scout ○ Other _____ ○ None?
16. Favorite Girl Scout cookie? _____
17. Lucky charm or something lucky you wear? ○ No ○ Yes, _____.
18. Ever run a lemonade stand? ○ Yes ○ No
19. Kind of business you'd like to start someday? _____
20. I would love to be president of _____.

Twofers

Name ( )

1. Fave sweet and salty combo? _____

2. Reasons for being late? _____

3. Things you always have with you? _____

4. Fave furry animals? _____

5. Habits you have? _____

6. Stuff outside your bedroom window? _____

7. Places you love? _____

8. Things you've climbed? _____

9. Words you really love? _____

10. Qualities you like in a friend? _____

11. Things that make you mad? _____

12. Fave animals that swim in the sea? _____

13. Green things you'll eat? _____

14. Black and white things you like? _____

15. Beverages you drink almost every day? _____

16. Things you love that fit in your hand? _____

17. Friends you talk to almost every day? _____

18. Colors you like to paint your toenails? _____

19. Stuff you've won? _____

20. Things you've lost? _____

1 question.
2 answers.

_____ forever.

_____

_____

_____ are so cute!

_____

_____

_____

_____ are awesome words!

_____

_____

_____

_____

_____

_____

_____ are my favorites.

_____

_____ are missing.

1. Name ⬭

2. Leopard prints are so ○ chic ○ tacky?

3. ○ Seven dwarves ○ One fairy godmother?

4. How many tiaras do you own? ⬭

5. Mannequins give you the creeps? ○ No ○ Yes

6. Ever been in a corn maze? ○ Yes ○ No ○ Not sure, what is that?

7. Last school project you did? _____

8. British accents sound ○ so cool ○ smart ○ kinda snobby?

9. ○ Pair of glass slippers ○ Pumpkin that turns into a carriage?

10. Magic ○ potion ○ wand ○ markers?

11. ○ Sand between your toes ○ Out too deep to touch bottom?

12. Bowling? ○ Ridiculous ○ Fun ○ Ridiculously fun!

13. What do you talk about more than anything? _____

14. Would you rather be a ○ princess ○ princess' sister?

15. Skinny jeans with ○ flats ○ flip-flops ○ sneakers?

16. Today are you ○ fairest of them all ○ "sleepy" beauty?

17. Three words to describe your life? _____

18. Favorite song to sing with friends? _____

19. How 'bout to dance to with friends? _____

20. I wish I were a(n) ○ English ○ history ○ math ○ science whiz!

Who's the worst of the fairy tale foes?

○ Wicked queen stepmother

○ Super mean stepsisters

○ Other

_____

_____

coke OR pepsi?

classic

● Coke ● Pepsi?

● Hot dog ● Hamburger?

● Milk ● Dark chocolate?

● Butterflies ● Dragonflies?

● Small talk
● Deep conversation?

● Sneakers ● Flip-flops?

Best movie ever? _____

_____

Worst movie ever? _____

_____

Favorite number? Why? _____

_____

● Reality show ● Sitcom?

● Bicycle through Europe
● African safari?

What scares you? _____

_____

Fave school subject? _____

_____

I LOVE TWISTER!

1. Name _____

2. Which have you taken a ride on? ○ **Horse** ○ **Elephant** ○ **Camel** ○ **None!**

3. Team(s) you like to root for? _____

4. Favorite pasta topping? ○ Meatballs ○ Cheese ○ Other_____

5. ○ Pencil ○ Pen ○ Keyboard?

6. Own a pair of boots? ○ **No** ○ **Yes,** (_____) **pairs.**

7. How 'bout a cowboy hat? ○ Yep ○ No way

8. Like peanut butter? ○ No ○ Yes, _____ is my favorite kind.

9. Think quiet people are ○ smart ○ shy ○ not interested?

10. Ideal summer vacation? _____

11. Play a mean game of ping pong? ○ Yep, I'm awesome. ○ I'm OK. ○ No!

12. Last time you played Twister? _____

13. ○ Zoo ○ Aquarium ○ Neither, I like animals in the wild.

14. Do you like Scrabble? ○ Yes ○ No

15. Singer/Band that appears the most on your playlists? _____

16. ZOMBIES ARE CHASING YOU. WHO DO YOU WANT WITH YOU? _____

17. Huge sale at the mall. Who would you want with you? _____

18. Tried raw oysters? ○ No ○ Yes Did you like? ○ No! Ick! ○ Yes

19. Three things for a perfect weekend? _____

20. Own anything with polka dots on it? ○ Of course ○ Nope

coke-or-pepsi.com

I AM NOT A BRAT!

1. Name _____

2. Last thing you put ketchup on? _____

3. ○ Goldfish ○ Hermit crab ○ Iguana ○ Gross! None!

4. Musical instrument you gave up? _____

5. ○ Online ○ Phone?

6. How many cousins do you have? _____

7. Ever been on YouTube? ○ Yes ○ No

8. If yes, what for? _____

9. Which is cuter? ○ Rabbit ○ Guinea pig

10. Use a calendar? ○ Yes ○ No

11. Coolest thing about your pet? _____

12. Currently ○ in braces ○ wearing a retainer ○ free of devices!

13. Last flick you cried at? _____

14. Text/Chat abbreviation you use a lot? _____

15. Are you a brat? ○ No ○ Sometimes ○ Pretty much

16. Sport you gave up? _____

17. Who thinks just like you? _____

18. ○ East Coast ○ West Coast ○ In the Middle?

19. First thing you do when you wake up? _____

20. What do you want to be doing by age 25? _____

Name

Why were you named that?

Do you like it?

■ Yes   No ■

Fave thing that comes in a wrapper?

Would you rather ...

■ Swim like a dolphin   ■ Fly like an eagle?

Can you tie a good bow?

■ Yes   No ■

Where would you swim to?   Where would you fly to?

Do you interrrupt people?

■ Yes   ■ No
☹   ☺

■ Shake   ■ Malt →   What IS malt?

Fave flave?

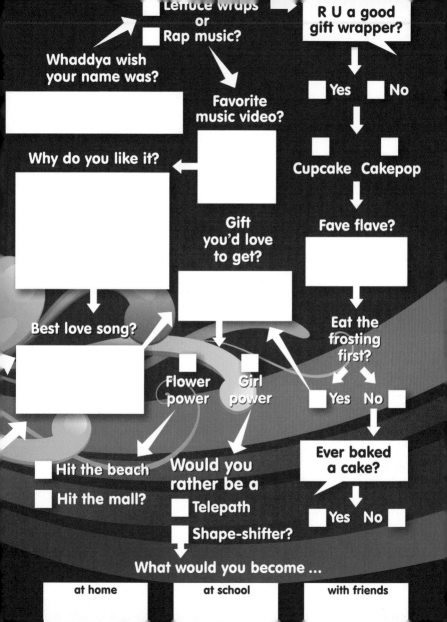

Flower power girl power

1. Name _____

2. How tall are you? _____

3. Super nice to someone this week? ○ Yes 😊 ○ No

4. Most glamorous thing you own? _____

5. Time you wake up on a school day? _____

6. Time you wake up on the weekend? _____

7. If you could be an Olympian, which sport would you choose? _____

8. Everything tastes better with _____.

9. Ever had dessert for breakfast? ○ Oh yeah ○ Nope

10. ○ Throw away ○ Donate ○ Keep too much?

11. Band you would love to tour with? _____

12. Would you add color stripes to your hair? ○ No ○ Yes ○ Already did!

13. Favorite teacher? _____

14. ○ Relax in a pair of jeans ○ Twirl in a beautiful ball gown?

15. Coconut ○ cream pie ○ cake ○ not a coconut fan

16. Snow ○ cone ○ day ○ sledding?

17. Best party you've gone to? _____

18. Crush know you exist? ○ Yes ○ No ○ Don't have one

19. Where are you in family's birth order? _____

20. When you tell a story, do you ○ exaggerate ○ stick to the facts ○ do both?

PEACE FOREVER

1. Name ⬭

2. I'm wearing ◯ lip gloss ◯ nail polish ◯ neither.

3. Which is worse? ◯ Homework ◯ Cleaning your room

4. How many pillows do you sleep with? ⬭

5. Favorite window to look out? _____

6. Something a parent does that drives you nuts? _____

7. Actress you would love to be a personal assistant to? _____

8. Are you more of a ◯ pants ◯ skirt girl?

9. If you could change one thing today, what would it be? _____

10. If you were an instrument, what would you be? _____

11. Best part of being a super heroine? ◯ Power ◯ Costume ◯ Cool name

12. If you could only visit 1 Website this month, which would it be? _____

13. Best class trip ever? _____

14. Quality a friend has you wished you had? _____

15. One weird fact you know? _____

16. Coolest thing you've ever found? _____

17. Know anything about family ancestors? ◯ No ◯ Yes, _____.

18. Fave sleepover snacks? _____

19. Coordinate shoes and bag? ◯ Always ◯ Sometimes ◯ Who cares?

20. If you had a safe, what would you keep in it? _____

If you were...

Name _____

1. **a mermaid,** where in the world would you want to live? Why?

   _____

2. **President,** what kind of room would you add to the White House?

   _____

3. an exotic **animal keeper,** which animals would you want to care for?

   _____

4. **in charge** of naming the next kind of American spacecraft, what awesome
   name would you give it? _____

5. **a dog,** which neighborhood dogs would you want to hang with? Why?

   _____

6. **a teacher,** what cool activity would you do with your class?

   _____

7. **in charge of your school** for a day, what would you change?

   _____

8. **going to live** on the moon for one year who would you take with you?
   Why? _____

9. **able to stay** the same age for the rest of your life, which age would you
   pick? Why? _____

10. able to have any **talent** you don't currently have, what would it be?

   _____

First thing that comes to mind when you see or hear these words?

(another word, sentence, or super short story)

1. Panda bear . . . .
2. Hysterical . . . .
3. Fireworks . . . .
4. T-shirt . . . .
5. Marshmallow . . . .
6. Celery sticks . . . .
7. Raisins . . . .
8. Poodle . . . .
9. Sunglasses . . . .
10. Chucks . . . .
11. Stick people . . . .
12. Physical Education . . . .
13. Mountain . . . .
14. Scooter . . . .
15. Pyramid . . . .
16. Diamonds . . . .
17. Hot peppers . . . .
18. Ringtone . . . .
19. Nail polish . . . .
20. Alligator . . . .

Name

1. Name (_____)

2. ○ Cinnamon ○ Fruity ○ Minty gum?

3. What do you love about yourself? _____

4. Where were you last time you used mustard? _____

5. The last paper I wrote for a class was about _____

_____ .

6. I could never eat _____ again and be OK.

7. TV show you most belong on? _____

8. WOULD YOU RATHER BE THE ○ STAR ON A LOSING TEAM ○ WORST ON A STAR TEAM?

9. Ever carved anything in a tree? ○ Yes ○ No

10. ○ Swim with the dolphins ○ Pet a manatee?

11. Would you rather be a ○ giant ○ pixie?

12. ○ Fuzzy socks ○ Warm slippers?

13. Hot chocolate ○ with ○ without marshmallows?

14. Good at sneaking up on people? ○ Not really ○ Kind of ○ Absolutely!

15. Scariest thing you've done on purpose? _____

16. New pair of ○ jeans ○ shoes?

17. If I could _____ , I would be thrilled.

18. Age you turned on fave birthday? (_____)

19. Something you would love to see?_____

20. Which is worse? ○ Really sad ○ Out-of-control mad

○ Potato chips
○ French fries?

○ Fashionable
○ Casual?

○ Sunset
○ Sunrise?

○ Brownies
○ Chocolate chip cookies?

coke
OR
pepsi?

classic

Best holiday? (   )

Fave actor? (   )

Fave actress?
(   )

One word to
describe you?
(   )

○ Big Mac
○ Whopper?

○ Gold
○ Silver?

coke-or-pepsi.com

1. Name _____

2. ○ Skinny jeans ○ Jeggings ○ Neither?

3. *Happiest color?* _____

4. **What were you doing in the last photo taken of you?** _____

5. Where were you? _____

6. **Know how to cook?** ○ **No** ○ **A little** ○ **Yes**

7. If yes to #6, what's your specialty? _____

8. Are you usually ○ cold ○ hot?

9. Famous person you admire most? _____

10. **DO HORROR MOVIES FRIGHTEN YOU?** ○ **NOT REALLY** ○ **YES, NIGHTMARES!**

11. Fave outfit to relax in? _____

12. Ever shoot a spitball? ○ Yes ○ Gross, no!

13. **Favorite thing that comes in your mail?** _____.

14. Sprinkles ○ always make me happy ○ are kinda overrated.

15. **Any phobias or fears?** ○ **Nope** ○ **Yes, I'm afraid of** _____.

16. ○ Drama queen ○ Cool, calm, and collected?

17. What do you crave? _____

18. Drink after other people? ○ Yeah ○ Sometimes ○ Never! Germs!

19. Ever encountered a bat? ○ Yes ○ No

20. What do you hear right now? _____

Ahh! You're going to wear that?

Scare-crow! Caww!

1. Name _____

2. Afraid to cross bridges? ○ Yes ○ No

3. Can you wiggle your ears without using your hands? ○ No ○ Yes

4. Do you ○ give in ○ get your way?

5. LAST THING YOU SOLD FOR YOUR SCHOOL? _____

6. Go to the library? ○ No ○ Yes

7. Longest word you know? _____

8. Can you hang a spoon from your nose? ○ Yes ○ No ○ Huh?

9. Best food with a glass of milk? _____

10. Gold ○ fish ○ bracelet?

11. Any strange talent? ○ No ○ Yes, I _____.

12. Spend the night in a haunted house? ○ NO! ○ Sure, I don't believe.

13. It's scary how much I like _____.

14. Give good manicures? ○ Yes ○ No

15. Favorite reality show? _____

16. Scrambled eggs are ○ yummy ○ frightening.

17. Worst thing about your brother(s)/sister(s)? _____

18. Best thing about your brother(s)/sister(s)? _____

19. LOVE A GOOD MYSTERY? ○ YES! ○ NAH

20. Think you're creative? ○ Yes ○ A little ○ Not really

Name _____

1. swim with a huge, harmless whale in the ocean, would you? ○ Yes ○ No, but I would swim with _____.

2. slow down time, which event would you slow down? _____

3. add sisters or brothers to your family, which genders and ages would you choose?

_____

4. have absolutely anything for dinner tonight, what would you pick? _____

_____

5. do one fun thing with an alien visiting our planet, what would it be? _____

_____

6. become any object for just one day, what would you be? Why? _____

_____

7. be an exchange student for one year anywhere in the world, which country would you visit? _____

8. be great friends with someone from the past, who would you choose? Why?

_____

9. do absolutely anything for just one year, what would you do? _____

_____

10. change your last name, without hurting your parents' feelings, would you?
    ○ No ○ Yes, I would change it to _____.

coke-or-pepsi.com

First thing that comes to mind when you see or hear these words?

(another word, sentence, or super short story)

Name

1. Corn on the cob . . . .

2. Dark alley . . . .

3. Roller coaster . . . .

4. Pigs in blankets . . . .

5. Hamster . . . .

6. Pink . . . .

7. Glow-in-the-dark . . . .

8. The letter U . . . .

9. Hello Kitty . . . .

10. Face painting . . . .

11. Super star . . . .

12. Bell . . . .

13. Sleeping bag . . . .

14. Hollywood . . . .

15. Rock . . . .

16. Piano . . . .

17. Magazine . . . .

18. Watermelon . . . .

19. Bubbles . . . .

20. Subway . . . .

classic

- ○ Waffle cone
- ○ Sugar cone
- ○ Cup?

- ○ Ice cubes
- ○ Crushed ice?

- ○ TV
- ○ Book?

- ○ Beach
- ○ Mountains?

- ○ Go with the flow
- ○ Stick to a routine?

- ○ Ice cream
- ○ Fro-yo?

Favorite relative?

Best amusement park ride?

Favorite game?

Best book?

coke-or-pepsi.com

Last things i painted were my nails

1. Name _____

2. Best thing in a spray can? ○ **Whipped Cream** ○ **Cheese Whiz** ○ **Paint**

3. Ever sprayed whipped cream directly in your mouth? ○ Yes ○ No

4. Last thing you painted? _____

5. Last thing you had stuck in your hair? _____

6. ○ Donuts ○ Donut holes

7. Worse T-shirt color? ○ Orange ○ Yellow ○ Green

8. What are you a beginner at? _____

9. What are you an expert at? _____

10. Favorite dip? _____

11. Favorite thing to dip? _____

12. Scarves? ○ Luv 'em ○ Hate 'em, so restricting!

13. I heart _____.

14. _____ is epic.

15. Friend with the coolest family? _____

16. ○ Red velvet cheesecake brownie ○ S'more-stuffed chocolate chip cookie?

17. Fave flave for lipgloss? _____

18. Favorite emoticon? _____

19. ○ Abracadabra ○ Bipiddi-boppidi-boo ○ Expelliarmus?

20. ○ Lemonade ○ Pink Lemonade?

I like movies that make me cry

1. Name _____

2. Last animated movie you saw? _____

3. Movies ○ with happy endings ○ that leave you thinking?

4. Sleepovers? ○ Fun! ○ Ugh.

5. ○ French Bulldog ○ Irish Setter ○ Alaskan Husky?

6. **Movies** ○ **at the theater** ○ **at home?**

7. Are you a ○ share-your-umbrella ○ every-girl-for-herself kinda girl?

8. ○ Polo ○ Graphic Tee?

9. Love to see a ○ volcano erupt ○ total eclipse of the sun?

10. What does your hair do on rainy days? _____

11. ○ **Write a great novel** ○ **Travel around the world?**

12. ○ Hike through the woods ○ Stroll through the city?

13. Ever danced the hula? ○ Yes ○ No

14. **Very first song you remember liking?** _____

15. Maple syrup on ○ waffles ○ French toast?

16. Ever fallen backwards in a chair? ○ Yes ○ No

17. **Wear shoes in the house?** ○ **Yes** ○ **Sometimes** ○ **Never**

18. If you get married, will you ○ keep ○ ditch ○ combine your last name(s)?

19. ○ Pack light ○ Certified overpacker?

20. FAVE SONG TO SING ON ROCK BAND OR GUITAR HERO? _____

I'll never get rid of my chucks

1. Name _____

2. On anyone's bad side right now? ○ Yes ○ No

3. WORN-OUT ITEM YOU CAN'T PART WITH? _____

4. ○ Italian ice ○ French vanilla ice cream ○ German chocolate cake?

5. Most unusual animal you've ever fed? _____

6. When things get hard, do you usually ○ give up ○ keep trying?

7. SCHOOL UNIFORMS? ○ FOR IT ○ AGAINST?

8. ○ Sweater ○ Hoodie?

9. One thing you'd like to learn to do well? _____

10. Pigs are ○ so cute ○ muddy, stinky, and gross.

11. Wear glitter? ○ Yes, love the sparkle! ○ Nah, too gaudy.

12. Glow sticks? ○ Still fun ○ Ho hum

13. Last thing you do before you turn off the lights? _____

14. Love ○ notes ○ letter ○ potion?

15. ○ Brownie ○ Girl Scout ○ Other _____ ○ None?

16. Favorite Girl Scout cookie? _____

17. Lucky charm or something lucky you wear? ○ No ○ Yes, _____.

18. Ever run a lemonade stand? ○ Yes ○ No

19. Kind of business you'd like to start someday? _____

20. I would love to be president of _____.

Twofers

Name ( )

1. **Fave sweet and salty combo?** _____

2. Reasons for being late? _____

3. **Things you always have with you?** _____

4. Fave furry animals? _____

5. **Habits you have?** _____

6. Stuff outside your bedroom window? _____

7. **Places you love?** _____

8. Things you've climbed? _____

9. **Words you really love?** _____

10. Qualities you like in a friend? _____

11. **Things that make you mad?** _____

12. Fave animals that swim in the sea? _____

13. **Green things you'll eat?** _____

14. Black and white things you like? _____

15. **Beverages you drink almost every day?** _____

16. Things you love that fit in your hand? _____

17. **Friends you talk to almost every day?** _____

18. Colors you like to paint your toenails? _____

19. **Stuff you've won?** _____

20. Things you've lost? _____

1 question.
2 answers.

_____ forever.
_____
_____
_____ are so cute!
_____
_____
_____ are awesome words!
_____
_____
_____
_____
_____
_____
_____ are my favorites.
_____
_____ are missing.

1. Name [_____]

2. Leopard prints are so ○ chic ○ tacky?

3. ○ Seven dwarves ○ One fairy godmother?

4. How many tiaras do you own? [_____]

5. Mannequins give you the creeps? ○ No ○ Yes

6. Ever been in a corn maze? ○ Yes ○ No ○ Not sure, what is that?

7. Last school project you did? _____

8. British accents sound ○ so cool ○ smart ○ kinda snobby?

9. ○ Pair of glass slippers ○ Pumpkin that turns into a carriage?

10. Magic ○ potion ○ wand ○ markers?

11. ○ Sand between your toes ○ Out too deep to touch bottom?

12. Bowling? ○ Ridiculous ○ Fun ○ Ridiculously fun!

13. What do you talk about more than anything? _____

14. Would you rather be a ○ princess ○ princess' sister?

15. Skinny jeans with ○ flats ○ flip-flops ○ sneakers?

16. Today are you ○ fairest of them all ○ "sleepy" beauty?

17. Three words to describe your life? _____

18. Favorite song to sing with friends? _____

19. How 'bout to dance to with friends? _____

20. I wish I were a(n) ○ English ○ history ○ math ○ science whiz!

Who's the worst of the fairy tale foes?

TALKING MIRRORS

Fact or Fiction

○ Wicked queen stepmother

○ Super mean stepsisters

○ Other

_____

_____

⬤ Coke ⬤ Pepsi?

⬤ Hot dog ⬤ Hamburger?

⬤ Milk ⬤ Dark chocolate?

⬤ Butterflies ⬤ Dragonflies?

⬤ Small talk
⬤ Deep conversation?

⬤ Sneakers ⬤ Flip-flops?

Best movie ever? _____

_____

Worst movie ever? _____

_____

Favorite number? Why? _____

_____

⬤ Reality show ⬤ Sitcom?

⬤ Bicycle through Europe
⬤ African safari?

What scares you? _____

_____

Fave school subject? _____

_____

I LOVE TWISTER!

1. Name

2. Which have you taken a ride on? ○ **Horse** ○ **Elephant** ○ **Camel** ○ **None!**

3. Team(s) you like to root for? _____

4. Favorite pasta topping? ○ Meatballs ○ Cheese ○ Other_____

5. ○ Pencil ○ Pen ○ Keyboard?

6. Own a pair of boots? ○ **No** ○ **Yes,** (_____) **pairs.**

7. How 'bout a cowboy hat? ○ Yep ○ No way

8. Like peanut butter? ○ No ○ Yes, _____ is my favorite kind.

9. Think quiet people are ○ smart ○ shy ○ not interested?

10. Ideal summer vacation? _____

11. Play a mean game of ping pong? ○ Yep, I'm awesome. ○ I'm OK. ○ No!

12. Last time you played Twister? _____

13. ○ Zoo ○ Aquarium ○ Neither, I like animals in the wild.

14. Do you like Scrabble? ○ Yes ○ No

15. Singer/Band that appears the most on your playlists? _____

16. ZOMBIES ARE CHASING YOU. WHO DO YOU WANT WITH YOU? _____

17. Huge sale at the mall. Who would you want with you? _____

18. Tried raw oysters? ○ No ○ Yes Did you like? ○ No! Ick! ○ Yes

19. Three things for a perfect weekend? _____

20. Own anything with polka dots on it? ○ Of course ○ Nope

coke-or-pepsi.com

I AM NOT A BRAT!

1. Name (   )

2. Last thing you put ketchup on? _____

3. ○ Goldfish ○ Hermit crab ○ Iguana ○ Gross! None!

4. Musical instrument you gave up? _____

5. ○ Online ○ Phone?

6. How many cousins do you have? (   )

7. Ever been on YouTube? ○ Yes ○ No

8. If yes, what for? _____

9. Which is cuter? ○ Rabbit ○ Guinea pig

10. Use a calendar? ○ Yes ○ No

11. Coolest thing about your pet? _____

12. Currently ○ in braces ○ wearing a retainer ○ free of devices!

13. Last flick you cried at? _____

14. Text/Chat abbreviation you use a lot? _____

15. Are you a brat? ○ No ○ Sometimes ○ Pretty much

16. Sport you gave up? _____

17. Who thinks just like you? _____

18. ○ East Coast ○ West Coast ○ In the Middle?

19. First thing you do when you wake up? _____

20. What do you want to be doing by age 25? _____

flower power
girl power

1. Name

2. How tall are you? _____

3. Super nice to someone this week? ○ Yes 🙂 ○ No

4. Most glamorous thing you own? _____

5. Time you wake up on a school day?

6. Time you wake up on the weekend?

7. If you could be an Olympian, which sport would you choose? _____

8. Everything tastes better with _____.

9. Ever had dessert for breakfast? ○ Oh yeah ○ Nope

10. ○ Throw away ○ Donate ○ Keep too much?

11. Band you would love to tour with? _____

12. Would you add color stripes to your hair? ○ No ○ Yes ○ Already did!

13. Favorite teacher? _____

14. ○ **Relax in a pair of jeans** ○ **Twirl in a beautiful ball gown?**

15. Coconut ○ cream pie ○ cake ○ not a coconut fan

16. Snow ○ cone ○ day ○ sledding?

17. Best party you've gone to? _____

18. Crush know you exist? ○ **Yes** ○ **No** ○ **Don't have one**

19. Where are you in family's birth order? _____

20. When you tell a story, do you ○ exaggerate ○ stick to the facts ○ do both?

PEACE FOREVER

1. Name _____

2. I'm wearing ○ lip gloss ○ nail polish ○ neither.

3. Which is worse? ○ Homework ○ Cleaning your room

4. How many pillows do you sleep with? _____

5. Favorite window to look out? _____

6. Something a parent does that drives you nuts? _____

7. Actress you would love to be a personal assistant to? _____

8. Are you more of a ○ pants ○ skirt girl?

9. If you could change one thing today, what would it be? _____

10. If you were an instrument, what would you be? _____

11. Best part of being a super heroine? ○ Power ○ Costume ○ Cool name

12. If you could only visit 1 Website this month, which would it be? _____

13. Best class trip ever? _____

14. Quality a friend has you wished you had? _____

15. One weird fact you know? _____

16. Coolest thing you've ever found? _____

17. Know anything about family ancestors? ○ No ○ Yes, _____.

18. Fave sleepover snacks? _____

19. Coordinate shoes and bag? ○ Always ○ Sometimes ○ Who cares?

20. If you had a safe, what would you keep in it? _____

If you were ...

Name

1. **a mermaid,** where in the world would you want to live? Why?

_____

2. **President,** what kind of room would you add to the White House?

_____

3. an exotic **animal keeper,** which animals would you want to care for?

_____

4. **in charge** of naming the next kind of American spacecraft, what awesome name would you give it? _____

5. **a dog,** which neighborhood dogs would you want to hang with? Why?

_____

6. **a teacher,** what cool activity would you do with your class?

_____

7. **in charge of your school** for a day, what would you change?

_____

8. **going to live** on the moon for one year who would you take with you? Why? _____

9. **able to stay** the same age for the rest of your life, which age would you pick? Why? _____

10. able to have any **talent** you don't currently have, what would it be?

_____

First thing that comes to mind when you see or hear these words?

(another word, sentence, or super short story)

1. Panda bear . . . .
2. Hysterical . . . .
3. Fireworks . . . .
4. T-shirt . . . .
5. Marshmallow . . . .
6. Celery sticks . . . .
7. Raisins . . . .
8. Poodle . . . .
9. Sunglasses . . . .
10. Chucks . . . .
11. Stick people . . . .
12. Physical Education . . . .
13. Mountain . . . .
14. Scooter . . . .
15. Pyramid . . . .
16. Diamonds . . . .
17. Hot peppers . . . .
18. Ringtone . . . .
19. Nail polish . . . .
20. Alligator . . . .

Name

1. Name (_____)

2. ◯ Cinnamon ◯ Fruity ◯ Minty gum?

3. What do you love about yourself? _____

4. Where were you last time you used mustard? _____

5. The last paper I wrote for a class was about _____

_____ .

6. I could never eat _____ again and be OK.

7. TV show you most belong on? _____

8. WOULD YOU RATHER BE THE ◯ STAR ON A LOSING TEAM ◯ WORST ON A STAR TEAM?

9. Ever carved anything in a tree? ◯ Yes ◯ No

10. ◯ Swim with the dolphins ◯ Pet a manatee?

11. Would you rather be a ◯ giant ◯ pixie?

12. ◯ Fuzzy socks ◯ Warm slippers?

13. Hot chocolate ◯ with ◯ without marshmallows?

14. Good at sneaking up on people? ◯ Not really ◯ Kind of ◯ Absolutely!

15. Scariest thing you've done on purpose? _____

16. New pair of ◯ jeans ◯ shoes?

17. If I could _____ , I would be thrilled.

18. Age you turned on fave birthday? (_____)

19. Something you would love to see?_____

20. Which is worse? ◯ Really sad ◯ Out-of-control mad

○ Potato chips
○ French fries?

coke OR pepsi?

○ Fashionable
○ Casual?

classic

○ Sunset
○ Sunrise?

○ Brownies
○ Chocolate chip cookies?

Best holiday? ( )

Fave actor? ( )

Fave actress?
( )

One word to describe you?
( )

○ Big Mac
○ Whopper?

○ Gold
○ Silver?

coke-or-pepsi.com

1. Name [   ]

2. ◯ Skinny jeans ◯ Jeggings ◯ Neither?

3. *Happiest color?* _____

4. What were you doing in the last photo taken of you? _____

5. Where were you? _____

6. Know how to cook? ◯ No ◯ A little ◯ Yes

7. If yes to #6, what's your specialty? _____

8. Are you usually ◯ cold ◯ hot?

9. Famous person you admire most? _____

10. DO HORROR MOVIES FRIGHTEN YOU? ◯ NOT REALLY ◯ YES, NIGHTMARES!

11. Fave outfit to relax in? _____

12. Ever shoot a spitball? ◯ Yes ◯ Gross, no!

13. Favorite thing that comes in your mail? _____.

14. Sprinkles ◯ always make me happy ◯ are kinda overrated.

15. Any phobias or fears? ◯ Nope ◯ Yes, I'm afraid of _____.

16. ◯ Drama queen ◯ Cool, calm, and collected?

17. What do you crave? _____

18. Drink after other people? ◯ Yeah ◯ Sometimes ◯ Never! Germs!

19. Ever encountered a bat? ◯ Yes ◯ No

20. What do you hear right now? _____

Ahh! You're going to wear that?

Scare-crow! Caww!

1. Name _____

2. Afraid to cross bridges? ○ Yes ○ No

3. Can you wiggle your ears without using your hands? ○ No ○ Yes

4. Do you ○ give in ○ get your way?

5. LAST THING YOU SOLD FOR YOUR SCHOOL? _____

6. Go to the library? ○ No ○ Yes

7. Longest word you know? _____

8. Can you hang a spoon from your nose? ○ Yes ○ No ○ Huh?

9. Best food with a glass of milk? _____

10. Gold ○ fish ○ bracelet?

11. Any strange talent? ○ No ○ Yes, I _____.

12. Spend the night in a haunted house? ○ NO! ○ Sure, I don't believe.

13. It's scary how much I like _____.

14. Give good manicures? ○ Yes ○ No

15. Favorite reality show? _____

16. Scrambled eggs are ○ yummy ○ frightening.

17. Worst thing about your brother(s)/sister(s)? _____

18. Best thing about your brother(s)/sister(s)? _____

19. LOVE A GOOD MYSTERY? ○ YES! ○ NAH

20. Think you're creative? ○ Yes ○ A little ○ Not really

Name _____

1. swim with a huge, harmless whale in the ocean, would you? ○ Yes ○ No, but I would swim with _____.

2. slow down time, which event would you slow down? _____

3. add sisters or brothers to your family, which genders and ages would you choose?

   _____

4. have absolutely anything for dinner tonight, what would you pick? _____

   _____

5. do one fun thing with an alien visiting our planet, what would it be? _____

   _____

6. become any object for just one day, what would you be? Why? _____

   _____

7. be an exchange student for one year anywhere in the world, which country would you visit? _____

8. be great friends with someone from the past, who would you choose? Why?

   _____

9. do absolutely anything for just one year, what would you do? _____

   _____

10. change your last name, without hurting your parents' feelings, would you?

    ○ No ○ Yes, I would change it to _____.

coke-or-pepsi.com

First thing that comes to mind when you see or hear these words?

(another word, sentence, or super short story)

Name

1. Corn on the cob . . . .

2. Dark alley . . . .

3. Roller coaster . . . .

4. Pigs in blankets . . . .

5. Hamster . . . .

6. Pink . . . .

7. Glow-in-the-dark . . . .

8. The letter U . . . .

9. Hello Kitty . . . .

10. Face painting . . . .

11. Super star . . . .

12. Bell . . . .

13. Sleeping bag . . . .

14. Hollywood . . . .

15. Rock . . . .

16. Piano . . . .

17. Magazine . . . .

18. Watermelon . . . .

19. Bubbles . . . .

20. Subway . . . .

coke OR pepsi?

classic

- ○ Waffle cone
- ○ Sugar cone
- ○ Cup?

- ○ Ice cubes
- ○ Crushed ice?

- ○ TV
- ○ Book?

- ○ Beach
- ○ Mountains?

- ○ Go with the flow
- ○ Stick to a routine?

- ○ Ice cream
- ○ Fro-yo?

Favorite relative?

Best amusement park ride?

Favorite game?

Best book?

last things i painted were my nails

1. Name [   ]

2. Best thing in a spray can? ○ **Whipped Cream** ○ **Cheese Whiz** ○ **Paint**

3. Ever sprayed whipped cream directly in your mouth? ○ Yes ○ No

4. Last thing you painted? _____

5. Last thing you had stuck in your hair? _____

6. ○ Donuts ○ Donut holes

7. Worse T-shirt color? ○ **Orange** ○ **Yellow** ○ **Green**

8. What are you a beginner at? _____

9. What are you an expert at? _____

10. Favorite dip? _____

11. Favorite thing to dip? _____

12. Scarves? ○ Luv 'em ○ Hate 'em, so restricting!

13. I heart _____.

14. _____ is epic.

15. Friend with the coolest family? _____

16. ○ Red velvet cheesecake brownie ○ S'more-stuffed chocolate chip cookie?

17. Fave flave for lipgloss? _____

18. Favorite emoticon? _____

19. ○ Abracadabra ○ Bipiddi-boppidi-boo ○ Expelliarmus?

20. ○ Lemonade ○ Pink Lemonade?

I like movies that make me cry

1. Name

2. Last animated movie you saw? _____

3. Movies ◯ with happy endings ◯ that leave you thinking?

4. Sleepovers? ◯ Fun! ◯ Ugh.

5. ◯ French Bulldog ◯ Irish Setter ◯ Alaskan Husky?

6. **Movies** ◯ **at the theater** ◯ **at home?**

7. Are you a ◯ share-your-umbrella ◯ every-girl-for-herself kinda girl?

8. ◯ Polo ◯ Graphic Tee?

9. Love to see a ◯ volcano erupt ◯ total eclipse of the sun?

10. What does your hair do on rainy days? _____

11. ◯ **Write a great novel** ◯ **Travel around the world?**

12. ◯ Hike through the woods ◯ Stroll through the city?

13. Ever danced the hula? ◯ Yes ◯ No

14. **Very first song you remember liking?** _____

15. Maple syrup on ◯ waffles ◯ French toast?

16. Ever fallen backwards in a chair? ◯ Yes ◯ No

17. **Wear shoes in the house?** ◯ **Yes** ◯ **Sometimes** ◯ **Never**

18. If you get married, will you ◯ keep ◯ ditch ◯ combine your last name(s)?

19. ◯ Pack light ◯ Certified overpacker?

20. FAVE SONG TO SING ON ROCK BAND OR GUITAR HERO? _____

I'll never get rid of my chucks

1. Name
2. On anyone's bad side right now? ○ Yes ○ No
3. WORN-OUT ITEM YOU CAN'T PART WITH? _____
4. ○ Italian ice ○ French vanilla ice cream ○ German chocolate cake?
5. Most unusual animal you've ever fed? _____
6. When things get hard, do you usually ○ give up ○ keep trying?
7. SCHOOL UNIFORMS? ○ FOR IT ○ AGAINST?
8. ○ Sweater ○ Hoodie?
9. One thing you'd like to learn to do well? _____
10. Pigs are ○ so cute ○ muddy, stinky, and gross.
11. Wear glitter? ○ Yes, love the sparkle! ○ Nah, too gaudy.
12. Glow sticks? ○ Still fun ○ Ho hum
13. Last thing you do before you turn off the lights? _____
14. Love ○ notes ○ letter ○ potion?
15. ○ Brownie ○ Girl Scout ○ Other _____ ○ None?
16. Favorite Girl Scout cookie? _____
17. Lucky charm or something lucky you wear? ○ No ○ Yes, _____.
18. Ever run a lemonade stand? ○ Yes ○ No
19. Kind of business you'd like to start someday? _____
20. I would love to be president of _____.

Twofers

Name

1. **Fave sweet and salty combo?**

2. Reasons for being late?

3. **Things you always have with you?**

4. Fave furry animals?

5. **Habits you have?**

6. Stuff outside your bedroom window?

7. **Places you love?**

8. Things you've climbed?

9. **Words you really love?**

10. Qualities you like in a friend?

11. **Things that make you mad?**

12. Fave animals that swim in the sea?

13. **Green things you'll eat?**

14. Black and white things you like?

15. **Beverages you drink almost every day?**

16. Things you love that fit in your hand?

17. **Friends you talk to almost every day?**

18. Colors you like to paint your toenails?

19. **Stuff you've won?**

20. Things you've lost?

1 question.
2 answers.

_____ forever.
_____
_____
_____ are so cute!
_____
_____
_____
_____ are awesome words!
_____
_____
_____
_____
_____
_____
_____ are my favorites.
_____
_____ are missing.

1. Name ⬭

2. Leopard prints are so ○ chic ○ tacky?

3. ○ **Seven dwarves** ○ **One fairy godmother?**

4. How many tiaras do you own? ⬭

5. Mannequins give you the creeps? ○ No ○ Yes

6. Ever been in a corn maze? ○ Yes ○ No ○ Not sure, what is that?

7. **Last school project you did?** _____

8. **British accents sound** ○ **so cool** ○ **smart** ○ **kinda snobby?**

9. ○ Pair of glass slippers ○ Pumpkin that turns into a carriage?

10. **Magic** ○ **potion** ○ **wand** ○ **markers?**

11. ○ Sand between your toes ○ Out too deep to touch bottom?

12. Bowling? ○ Ridiculous ○ Fun ○ Ridiculously fun!

13. **What do you talk about more than anything?** _____

14. Would you rather be a ○ princess ○ princess' sister?

15. Skinny jeans with ○ flats ○ flip-flops ○ sneakers?

16. Today are you ○ fairest of them all ○ "sleepy" beauty?

17. Three words to describe your life? _____

18. Favorite song to sing with friends? _____

19. How 'bout to dance to with friends? _____

20. **I wish I were a(n)** ○ **English** ○ **history** ○ **math** ○ **science whiz!**

Who's the worst of the fairy tale foes?

○ Wicked queen step-mother

○ Super mean step-sisters

○ Other

_____

_____

● Coke ● Pepsi?

● Hot dog ● Hamburger?

● Milk ● Dark chocolate?

● Butterflies ● Dragonflies?

● Small talk
● Deep conversation?

● Sneakers ● Flip-flops?

Best movie ever? _____

_____

Worst movie ever? _____

_____

Favorite number? Why? _____

_____

● Reality show ● Sitcom?

● Bicycle through Europe
● African safari?

What scares you? _____

_____

Fave school subject? _____

_____

I LOVE TWISTER!

1. Name [_____]

2. Which have you taken a ride on? ○ Horse ○ Elephant ○ Camel ○ None!

3. Team(s) you like to root for? _____

4. Favorite pasta topping? ○ Meatballs ○ Cheese ○ Other_____

5. ○ Pencil ○ Pen ○ Keyboard?

6. Own a pair of boots? ○ No ○ Yes, (____) pairs.

7. How 'bout a cowboy hat? ○ Yep ○ No way

8. Like peanut butter? ○ No ○ Yes, _____ is my favorite kind.

9. Think quiet people are ○ smart ○ shy ○ not interested?

10. Ideal summer vacation? _____

11. Play a mean game of ping pong? ○ Yep, I'm awesome. ○ I'm OK. ○ No!

12. Last time you played Twister? _____

13. ○ Zoo ○ Aquarium ○ Neither, I like animals in the wild.

14. Do you like Scrabble? ○ Yes ○ No

15. Singer/Band that appears the most on your playlists? _____

16. ZOMBIES ARE CHASING YOU. WHO DO YOU WANT WITH YOU? _____

17. Huge sale at the mall. Who would you want with you? _____

18. Tried raw oysters? ○ No ○ Yes Did you like? ○ No! Ick! ○ Yes

19. Three things for a perfect weekend? _____

20. Own anything with polka dots on it? ○ Of course ○ Nope

I AM NOT A BRAT!

1. Name _____

2. Last thing you put ketchup on? _____

3. ○ Goldfish ○ Hermit crab ○ Iguana ○ Gross! None!

4. Musical instrument you gave up? _____

5. ○ Online ○ Phone?

6. How many cousins do you have? _____

7. Ever been on YouTube? ○ Yes ○ No

8. If yes, what for? _____

9. Which is cuter? ○ Rabbit ○ Guinea pig

10. Use a calendar? ○ Yes ○ No

11. Coolest thing about your pet? _____

12. Currently ○ in braces ○ wearing a retainer ○ free of devices!

13. Last flick you cried at? _____

14. Text/Chat abbreviation you use a lot? _____

15. Are you a BRat? ○ No ○ Sometimes ○ Pretty much

16. Sport you gave up? _____

17. Who thinks just like you? _____

18. ○ East Coast ○ West Coast ○ In the Middle?

19. First thing you do when you wake up? _____

20. What do you want to be doing by age 25? _____

Why were you named that?

Name

Do you like it?
- Yes
- No

Fave thing that comes in a wrapper?

Would you rather ...
- Swim like a dolphin
- Fly like an eagle?

Can you tie a good bow?
- Yes
- No

Where would you swim to?

Where would you fly to?

Do you interrrrupt people?
- Yes ☹
- No ☺

- Shake
- Malt →

What IS malt?

Fave flave?

coke-or-pepsi.com

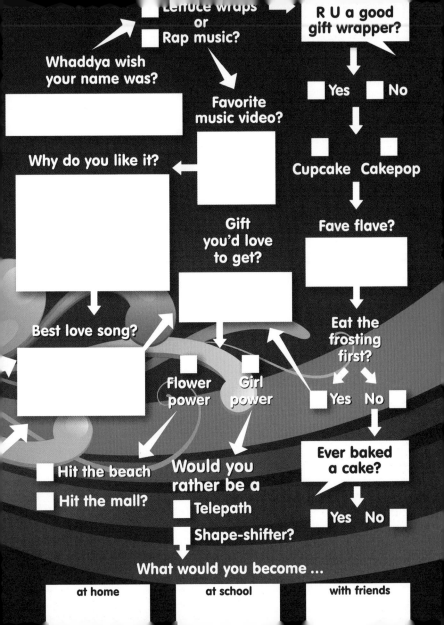

flower power
girl power

1. Name _____

2. How tall are you? _____

3. Super nice to someone this week? ○ Yes 😊 ○ No

4. Most glamorous thing you own? _____

5. Time you wake up on a school day? ( )

6. Time you wake up on the weekend? ( )

7. If you could be an Olympian, which sport would you choose? _____

8. Everything tastes better with _____ .

9. Ever had dessert for breakfast? ○ Oh yeah ○ Nope

10. ○ Throw away ○ Donate ○ Keep too much?

11. Band you would love to tour with? _____

12. Would you add color stripes to your hair? ○ No ○ Yes ○ Already did!

13. Favorite teacher? _____

14. ○ **Relax in a pair of jeans** ○ **Twirl in a beautiful ball gown?**

15. Coconut ○ cream pie ○ cake ○ not a coconut fan

16. Snow ○ cone ○ day ○ sledding?

17. Best party you've gone to? _____

18. Crush know you exist? ○ **Yes** ○ **No** ○ **Don't have one**

19. Where are you in family's birth order? _____

20. When you tell a story, do you ○ **exaggerate** ○ **stick to the facts** ○ **do both?**

PEACE FOREVER

1. Name _____

2. I'm wearing ◯ lip gloss ◯ nail polish ◯ neither.

3. Which is worse? ◯ Homework ◯ Cleaning your room

4. How many pillows do you sleep with? _____

5. Favorite window to look out? _____

6. Something a parent does that drives you nuts? _____

7. Actress you would love to be a personal assistant to? _____

8. Are you more of a ◯ pants ◯ skirt girl?

9. If you could change one thing today, what would it be? _____

10. If you were an instrument, what would you be? _____

11. Best part of being a super heroine? ◯ Power ◯ Costume ◯ Cool name

12. If you could only visit 1 Website this month, which would it be? _____

13. Best class trip ever? _____

14. Quality a friend has you wished you had? _____

15. One weird fact you know? _____

16. Coolest thing you've ever found? _____

17. Know anything about family ancestors? ◯ No ◯ Yes, _____.

18. Fave sleepover snacks? _____

19. Coordinate shoes and bag? ◯ Always ◯ Sometimes ◯ Who cares?

20. If you had a safe, what would you keep in it? _____

If you were ...

Name _____

1. a mermaid, where in the world would you want to live? Why?

   _____

2. President, what kind of room would you add to the White House?

   _____

3. an exotic animal keeper, which animals would you want to care for?

   _____

4. in charge of naming the next kind of American spacecraft, what awesome
   name would you give it? _____

5. a dog, which neighborhood dogs would you want to hang with? Why?

   _____

6. a teacher, what cool activity would you do with your class?

   _____

7. in charge of your school for a day, what would you change?

   _____

8. going to live on the moon for one year who would you take with you?
   Why? _____

9. able to stay the same age for the rest of your life, which age would you
   pick? Why? _____

10. able to have any talent you don't currently have, what would it be?

    _____

First thing that comes to mind when you see or hear these words?

(another word, sentence, or super short story)

1. Panda bear . . . .

2. Hysterical . . . .

3. Fireworks . . . .

4. T-shirt . . . .

5. Marshmallow . . . .

6. Celery sticks . . . .

7. Raisins . . . .

8. Poodle . . . .

9. Sunglasses . . . .

10. Chucks . . . .

11. Stick people . . . .

12. Physical Education . . . .

13. Mountain . . . .

14. Scooter . . . .

15. Pyramid . . . .

16. Diamonds . . . .

17. Hot peppers . . . .

18. Ringtone . . . .

19. Nail polish . . . .

20. Alligator . . . .

Name

1. Name (   )

2. ○ Cinnamon ○ Fruity ○ Minty gum?

3. What do you love about yourself? _____

4. Where were you last time you used mustard? _____

5. The last paper I wrote for a class was about _____

_____ .

6. I could never eat _____ again and be OK.

7. TV show you most belong on? _____

8. WOULD YOU RATHER BE THE ○ STAR ON A LOSING TEAM ○ WORST ON A STAR TEAM?

9. Ever carved anything in a tree? ○ Yes ○ No

10. ○ Swim with the dolphins   ○ Pet a manatee?

11. Would you rather be a ○ giant ○ pixie?

12. ○ Fuzzy socks ○ Warm slippers?

13. Hot chocolate ○ with ○ without marshmallows?

14. Good at sneaking up on people? ○ Not really ○ Kind of ○ Absolutely!

15. Scariest thing you've done on purpose? _____

16. New pair of ○ jeans ○ shoes?

17. If I could _____, I would be thrilled.

18. Age you turned on fave birthday? (   )

19. Something you would love to see?_____

20. Which is worse? ○ Really sad ○ Out-of-control mad

○ Potato chips
○ French fries?

coke OR pepsi?

○ Fashionable
○ Casual?

○ Sunset
○ Sunrise?

classic

○ Brownies
○ Chocolate chip cookies?

Best holiday? ( )

Fave actor? ( )

Fave actress?
( )

One word to
describe you?
( )

○ Big Mac
○ Whopper?

○ Gold
○ Silver?

coke-or-pepsi.com

forever

1. Name _____

2. ○ Skinny jeans ○ Jeggings ○ Neither?

3. *Happiest color?* _____

4. **What were you doing in the last photo taken of you?** _____

5. Where were you? _____

6. Know how to cook? ○ No ○ A little ○ Yes

7. If yes to #6, what's your specialty? _____

8. Are you usually ○ cold ○ hot?

9. Famous person you admire most? _____

10. DO HORROR MOVIES FRIGHTEN YOU? ○ NOT REALLY ○ YES, NIGHTMARES!

11. Fave outfit to relax in? _____

12. Ever shoot a spitball? ○ Yes ○ Gross, no!

13. Favorite thing that comes in your mail? _____.

14. Sprinkles ○ always make me happy ○ are kinda overrated.

15. Any phobias or fears? ○ Nope ○ Yes, I'm afraid of _____.

16. ○ Drama queen ○ Cool, calm, and collected?

17. What do you crave? _____

18. Drink after other people? ○ Yeah ○ Sometimes ○ Never! Germs!

19. Ever encountered a bat? ○ Yes ○ No

20. What do you hear right now? _____

coke-or-pepsi.com

Ahh! You're going to wear that?

Scare-crow! Caww!

1. Name

2. Afraid to cross bridges? ○ Yes ○ No

3. Can you wiggle your ears without using your hands? ○ No ○ Yes

4. Do you ○ give in ○ get your way?

5. LAST THING YOU SOLD FOR YOUR SCHOOL? _____

6. Go to the library? ○ No ○ Yes

7. Longest word you know? _____

8. Can you hang a spoon from your nose? ○ Yes ○ No ○ Huh?

9. Best food with a glass of milk? _____

10. Gold ○ fish ○ bracelet?

11. Any strange talent? ○ No ○ Yes, I _____.

12. Spend the night in a haunted house? ○ NO! ○ Sure, I don't believe.

13. It's scary how much I like _____.

14. Give good manicures? ○ Yes ○ No

15. Favorite reality show? _____

16. Scrambled eggs are ○ yummy ○ frightening.

17. Worst thing about your brother(s)/sister(s)? _____

18. Best thing about your brother(s)/sister(s)? _____

19. LOVE A GOOD MYSTERY? ○ YES! ○ NAH

20. Think you're creative? ○ Yes ○ A little ○ Not really

Name

1. swim with a huge, harmless whale in the ocean, would you? ○ Yes ○ No, but I would swim with _____.

2. slow down time, which event would you slow down? _____

3. add sisters or brothers to your family, which genders and ages would you choose?

_____

4. have absolutely anything for dinner tonight, what would you pick? _____

_____

5. do one fun thing with an alien visiting our planet, what would it be? _____

_____

6. become any object for just one day, what would you be? Why? _____

_____

7. be an exchange student for one year anywhere in the world, which country would you visit? _____

8. be great friends with someone from the past, who would you choose? Why?

_____

9. do absolutely anything for just one year, what would you do? _____

_____

10. change your last name, without hurting your parents' feelings, would you?
○ No ○ Yes, I would change it to _____.

coke-or-pepsi.com

First thing that comes to mind when you see or hear these words?

(another word, sentence, or super short story)

Name

1. Corn on the cob . . . .

2. Dark alley . . . .

3. Roller coaster . . . .

4. Pigs in blankets . . . .

5. Hamster . . . .

6. Pink . . . .

7. Glow-in-the-dark . . . .

8. The letter U . . . .

9. Hello Kitty . . . .

10. Face painting . . . .

11. Super star . . . .

12. Bell . . . .

13. Sleeping bag . . . .

14. Hollywood . . . .

15. Rock . . . .

16. Piano . . . .

17. Magazine . . . .

18. Watermelon . . . .

19. Bubbles . . . .

20. Subway . . . .

classic

○ Waffle cone
○ Sugar cone
○ Cup?

○ Ice cubes
○ Crushed ice?

○ TV
○ Book?

○ Beach
○ Mountains?

○ Go with the flow
○ Stick to a routine?

○ Ice cream
○ Fro-yo?

Favorite relative?

Best amusement park ride?

Favorite game?

Best book?

coke-or-pepsi.com

last things i painted were my nails

1. Name [_____]

2. Best thing in a spray can? ○ **Whipped Cream** ○ **Cheese Whiz** ○ **Paint**

3. Ever sprayed whipped cream directly in your mouth? ○ Yes ○ No

4. Last thing you painted? _____

5. Last thing you had stuck in your hair? _____

6. ○ Donuts ○ Donut holes

7. Worse T-shirt color? ○ **Orange** ○ **Yellow** ○ **Green**

8. What are you a beginner at? _____

9. What are you an expert at? _____

10. Favorite dip? _____

11. Favorite thing to dip? _____

12. Scarves? ○ Luv 'em ○ Hate 'em, so restricting!

13. I heart _____.

14. _____ is epic.

15. Friend with the coolest family? _____

16. ○ Red velvet cheesecake brownie ○ S'more-stuffed chocolate chip cookie?

17. Fave flave for lipgloss? _____

18. Favorite emoticon? _____

19. ○ Abracadabra ○ Bipiddi-boppidi-boo ○ Expelliarmus?

20. ○ Lemonade ○ Pink Lemonade?

I like movies that make me cry

1. Name

2. Last animated movie you saw? _____

3. Movies ○ with happy endings ○ that leave you thinking?

4. Sleepovers? ○ Fun! ○ Ugh.

5. ○ French Bulldog ○ Irish Setter ○ Alaskan Husky?

6. **Movies** ○ **at the theater** ○ **at home?**

7. Are you a ○ share-your-umbrella ○ every-girl-for-herself kinda girl?

8. ○ Polo ○ Graphic Tee?

9. Love to see a ○ volcano erupt ○ total eclipse of the sun?

10. What does your hair do on rainy days? _____

11. ○ **Write a great novel** ○ **Travel around the world?**

12. ○ Hike through the woods ○ Stroll through the city?

13. Ever danced the hula? ○ Yes ○ No

14. **Very first song you remember liking?** _____

15. Maple syrup on ○ waffles ○ French toast?

16. Ever fallen backwards in a chair? ○ Yes ○ No

17. **Wear shoes in the house?** ○ **Yes** ○ **Sometimes** ○ **Never**

18. If you get married, will you ○ keep ○ ditch ○ combine your last name(s)?

19. ○ Pack light ○ Certified overpacker?

20. FAVE SONG TO SING ON ROCK BAND OR GUITAR HERO? _____

I'll never get rid of my chucks

1. Name _____

2. On anyone's bad side right now? ○ Yes ○ No

3. WORN-OUT ITEM YOU CAN'T PART WITH? _____

4. ○ Italian ice ○ French vanilla ice cream ○ German chocolate cake?

5. Most unusual animal you've ever fed? _____

6. When things get hard, do you usually ○ give up ○ keep trying?

7. SCHOOL UNIFORMS? ○ FOR IT ○ AGAINST?

8. ○ Sweater ○ Hoodie?

9. One thing you'd like to learn to do well? _____

10. Pigs are ○ so cute ○ muddy, stinky, and gross.

11. Wear glitter? ○ Yes, love the sparkle! ○ Nah, too gaudy.

12. Glow sticks? ○ Still fun ○ Ho hum

13. Last thing you do before you turn off the lights? _____

14. Love ○ notes ○ letter ○ potion?

15. ○ Brownie ○ Girl Scout ○ Other _____ ○ None?

16. Favorite Girl Scout cookie? _____

17. Lucky charm or something lucky you wear? ○ No ○ Yes, _____.

18. Ever run a lemonade stand? ○ Yes ○ No

19. Kind of business you'd like to start someday? _____

20. I would love to be president of _____.

Twofers

Name (   )

1. **Fave sweet and salty combo?**_____

2. Reasons for being late?_____

3. **Things you always have with you?**_____

4. Fave furry animals?_____

5. **Habits you have?**_____

6. Stuff outside your bedroom window?_____

7. **Places you love?**_____

8. Things you've climbed?_____

9. **Words you really love?**_____

10. Qualities you like in a friend?_____

11. **Things that make you mad?**_____

12. Fave animals that swim in the sea?_____

13. **Green things you'll eat?**_____

14. Black and white things you like?_____

15. **Beverages you drink almost every day?**_____

16. Things you love that fit in your hand?_____

17. **Friends you talk to almost every day?**_____

18. Colors you like to paint your toenails?_____

19. **Stuff you've won?**_____

20. Things you've lost?_____

1 question.
2 answers.

_____ forever.

_____

_____

_____ are so cute!

_____

_____

_____

_____ are awesome words!

_____

_____

_____

_____

_____

_____

_____ are my favorites.

_____

_____ are missing.

1. Name [   ]

2. Leopard prints are so ○ chic ○ tacky?

3. ○ Seven dwarves ○ One fairy godmother?

4. How many tiaras do you own? [   ]

5. Mannequins give you the creeps? ○ No ○ Yes

6. Ever been in a corn maze? ○ Yes ○ No ○ Not sure, what is that?

7. Last school project you did? _____

8. British accents sound ○ so cool ○ smart ○ kinda snobby?

9. ○ Pair of glass slippers ○ Pumpkin that turns into a carriage?

10. Magic ○ potion ○ wand ○ markers?

11. ○ Sand between your toes ○ Out too deep to touch bottom?

12. Bowling? ○ Ridiculous ○ Fun ○ Ridiculously fun!

13. What do you talk about more than anything? _____

14. Would you rather be a ○ princess ○ princess' sister?

15. Skinny jeans with ○ flats ○ flip-flops ○ sneakers?

16. Today are you ○ fairest of them all ○ "sleepy" beauty?

17. Three words to describe your life? _____

18. Favorite song to sing with friends? _____

19. How 'bout to dance to with friends? _____

20. I wish I were a(n) ○ English ○ history ○ math ○ science whiz!

Who's the worst of the fairy tale foes?

○ Wicked queen step-mother

○ Super mean step-sisters

○ Other
_____
_____

● Coke ● Pepsi?

● Hot dog ● Hamburger?

● Milk ● Dark chocolate?

● Butterflies ● Dragonflies?

● Small talk
● Deep conversation?

● Sneakers ● Flip-flops?

Best movie ever? _____
_____

Worst movie ever? _____
_____

Favorite number? Why? _____
_____

● Reality show ● Sitcom?

● Bicycle through Europe
● African safari?

What scares you? _____
_____

Fave school subject? _____
_____

I LOVE TWISTER!

1. Name _____

2. Which have you taken a ride on? ○ **Horse** ○ **Elephant** ○ **Camel** ○ **None!**

3. Team(s) you like to root for? _____

4. Favorite pasta topping? ○ Meatballs ○ Cheese ○ Other_____

5. ○ Pencil ○ Pen ○ Keyboard?

6. Own a pair of boots? ○ **No** ○ **Yes,** (_____) **pairs.**

7. How 'bout a cowboy hat? ○ Yep ○ No way

8. Like peanut butter? ○ No ○ Yes, _____ is my favorite kind.

9. Think quiet people are ○ smart ○ shy ○ not interested?

10. Ideal summer vacation? _____

11. Play a mean game of ping pong? ○ Yep, I'm awesome. ○ I'm OK. ○ No!

12. Last time you played Twister? _____

13. ○ Zoo ○ Aquarium ○ Neither, I like animals in the wild.

14. Do you like Scrabble? ○ Yes ○ No

15. Singer/Band that appears the most on your playlists? _____

16. ZOMBIES ARE CHASING YOU. WHO DO YOU WANT WITH YOU? _____

17. Huge sale at the mall. Who would you want with you? _____

18. Tried raw oysters? ○ No ○ Yes Did you like? ○ No! Ick! ○ Yes

19. Three things for a perfect weekend? _____

20. Own anything with polka dots on it? ○ Of course ○ Nope

coke-or-pepsi.com

I AM NOT A BRAT!

1. Name [_____]

2. Last thing you put ketchup on? _____

3. ○ Goldfish ○ Hermit crab ○ Iguana ○ Gross! None!

4. Musical instrument you gave up? _____

5. ○ Online ○ Phone?

6. How many cousins do you have? [_____]

7. Ever been on YouTube? ○ Yes ○ No

8. If yes, what for? _____

9. Which is cuter? ○ Rabbit ○ Guinea pig

10. Use a calendar? ○ Yes ○ No

11. Coolest thing about your pet? _____

12. Currently ○ in braces ○ wearing a retainer ○ free of devices!

13. Last flick you cried at? _____

14. Text/Chat abbreviation you use a lot? _____

15. Are you a brat? ○ No ○ Sometimes ○ Pretty much

16. Sport you gave up? _____

17. Who thinks just like you? _____

18. ○ East Coast ○ West Coast ○ In the Middle?

19. First thing you do when you wake up? _____

20. What do you want to be doing by age 25? _____

Flower power girl power

1. Name

2. How tall are you? _____

3. Super nice to someone this week? ○ Yes 😊 ○ No

4. **Most glamorous thing you own?** _____

5. Time you wake up on a school day?

6. Time you wake up on the weekend?

7. If you could be an Olympian, which sport would you choose? _____

8. Everything tastes better with _____.

9. Ever had dessert for breakfast? ○ Oh yeah ○ Nope

10. ○ Throw away ○ Donate ○ Keep too much?

11. **Band you would love to tour with?** _____

12. Would you add color stripes to your hair? ○ No ○ Yes ○ Already did!

13. Favorite teacher? _____

14. ○ **Relax in a pair of jeans** ○ **Twirl in a beautiful ball gown?**

15. Coconut ○ cream pie ○ cake ○ not a coconut fan

16. Snow ○ cone ○ day ○ sledding?

17. Best party you've gone to? _____

18. **Crush know you exist?** ○ **Yes** ○ **No** ○ **Don't have one**

19. Where are you in family's birth order? _____

20. When you tell a story, do you ○ exaggerate ○ stick to the facts ○ do both?

Peace Forever

1. Name [   ]

2. I'm wearing ○ lip gloss ○ nail polish ○ neither.

3. Which is worse? ○ Homework ○ Cleaning your room

4. How many pillows do you sleep with? [   ]

5. Favorite window to look out? _____

6. Something a parent does that drives you nuts? _____

7. Actress you would love to be a personal assistant to? _____

8. Are you more of a ○ pants ○ skirt girl?

9. If you could change one thing today, what would it be? _____

10. If you were an instrument, what would you be? _____

11. Best part of being a super heroine? ○ Power ○ Costume ○ Cool name

12. If you could only visit 1 Website this month, which would it be? _____

13. Best class trip ever? _____

14. Quality a friend has you wished you had? _____

15. One weird fact you know? _____

16. Coolest thing you've ever found? _____

17. Know anything about family ancestors? ○ No ○ Yes, _____.

18. Fave sleepover snacks? _____

19. Coordinate shoes and bag? ○ Always ○ Sometimes ○ Who cares?

20. If you had a safe, what would you keep in it? _____

If you were ...

Name

1. a mermaid, where in the world would you want to live? Why?

   _____

2. President, what kind of room would you add to the White House?

   _____

3. an exotic animal keeper, which animals would you want to care for?

   _____

4. in charge of naming the next kind of American spacecraft, what awesome

   name would you give it? _____

5. a dog, which neighborhood dogs would you want to hang with? Why?

   _____

6. a teacher, what cool activity would you do with your class?

   _____

7. in charge of your school for a day, what would you change?

   _____

8. going to live on the moon for one year who would you take with you?

   Why? _____

9. able to stay the same age for the rest of your life, which age would you

   pick? Why? _____

10. able to have any talent you don't currently have, what would it be?

    _____

First thing that comes to mind when you see or hear these words?

(another word, sentence, or super short story)

1. Panda bear . . . .
2. Hysterical . . . .
3. Fireworks . . . .
4. T-shirt . . . .
5. Marshmallow . . . .
6. Celery sticks . . . .
7. Raisins . . . .
8. Poodle . . . .
9. Sunglasses . . . .
10. Chucks . . . .
11. Stick people . . . .
12. Physical Education . . . .
13. Mountain . . . .
14. Scooter . . . .
15. Pyramid . . . .
16. Diamonds . . . .
17. Hot peppers . . . .
18. Ringtone . . . .
19. Nail polish . . . .
20. Alligator . . . .

Name

1. Name ( )

2. ○ Cinnamon ○ Fruity ○ Minty gum?

3. What do you love about yourself? _____

4. Where were you last time you used mustard? _____

5. The last paper I wrote for a class was about _____

_____ .

6. I could never eat _____ again and be OK.

7. TV show you most belong on? _____

8. WOULD YOU RATHER BE THE ○ STAR ON A LOSING TEAM ○ WORST ON A STAR TEAM?

9. Ever carved anything in a tree? ○ Yes ○ No

10. ○ Swim with the dolphins ○ Pet a manatee?

11. Would you rather be a ○ giant ○ pixie?

12. ○ Fuzzy socks ○ Warm slippers?

13. Hot chocolate ○ with ○ without marshmallows?

14. Good at sneaking up on people? ○ Not really ○ Kind of ○ Absolutely!

15. Scariest thing you've done on purpose? _____

16. New pair of ○ jeans ○ shoes?

17. If I could _____ , I would be thrilled.

18. Age you turned on fave birthday? ( )

19. Something you would love to see? _____

20. Which is worse? ○ Really sad ○ Out-of-control mad

○ Potato chips
○ French fries?

coke OR pepsi?

○ Fashionable
○ Casual?

○ Sunset
○ Sunrise?

classic

○ Brownies
○ Chocolate chip cookies?

Best holiday? (   )

Fave actor? (   )

Fave actress?
(   )

One word to
describe you?
(   )

○ Big Mac
○ Whopper?

○ Gold
○ Silver?

forever

1. Name _____

2. ○ Skinny jeans ○ Jeggings ○ Neither?

3. *Happiest color?* _____

4. What were you doing in the last photo taken of you? _____

5. Where were you? _____

6. **Know how to cook?** ○ **No** ○ **A little** ○ **Yes**

7. If yes to #6, what's your specialty? _____

8. Are you usually ○ cold ○ hot?

9. Famous person you admire most? _____

10. DO HORROR MOVIES FRIGHTEN YOU? ○ **NOT REALLY** ○ **YES, NIGHTMARES!**

11. Fave outfit to relax in? _____

12. Ever shoot a spitball? ○ Yes ○ Gross, no!

13. Favorite thing that comes in your mail? _____.

14. Sprinkles ○ always make me happy ○ are kinda overrated.

15. Any phobias or fears? ○ Nope ○ Yes, I'm afraid of _____.

16. ○ Drama queen ○ Cool, calm, and collected?

17. What do you crave? _____

18. Drink after other people? ○ Yeah ○ Sometimes ○ Never! Germs!

19. Ever encountered a bat? ○ Yes ○ No

20. What do you hear right now? _____

Ahh! You're going to wear that?

Scare- crow! Caww!

1. Name _____

2. Afraid to cross bridges? ○ Yes ○ No

3. Can you wiggle your ears without using your hands? ○ No ○ Yes

4. Do you ○ give in ○ get your way?

5. LAST THING YOU SOLD FOR YOUR SCHOOL? _____

6. Go to the library? ○ No ○ Yes

7. Longest word you know? _____

8. Can you hang a spoon from your nose? ○ Yes ○ No ○ Huh?

9. Best food with a glass of milk? _____

10. Gold ○ fish ○ bracelet?

11. Any strange talent? ○ No ○ Yes, I _____.

12. Spend the night in a haunted house? ○ NO! ○ Sure, I don't believe.

13. It's scary how much I like _____.

14. Give good manicures? ○ Yes ○ No

15. Favorite reality show? _____

16. Scrambled eggs are ○ yummy ○ frightening.

17. Worst thing about your brother(s)/sister(s)? _____

18. Best thing about your brother(s)/sister(s)? _____

19. LOVE A GOOD MYSTERY? ○ YES! ○ NAH

20. Think you're creative? ○ Yes ○ A little ○ Not really

Name

1. swim with a huge, harmless whale in the ocean, would you? ○Yes ○No, but I would swim with _____.

2. slow down time, which event would you slow down? _____

3. add sisters or brothers to your family, which genders and ages would you choose?

_____

4. have absolutely anything for dinner tonight, what would you pick? _____

_____

5. do one fun thing with an alien visiting our planet, what would it be? _____

_____

6. become any object for just one day, what would you be? Why? _____

_____

7. be an exchange student for one year anywhere in the world, which country would you visit? _____

8. be great friends with someone from the past, who would you choose? Why?

_____

9. do absolutely anything for just one year, what would you do? _____

_____

10. change your last name, without hurting your parents' feelings, would you?

○ No ○ Yes, I would change it to _____.

coke-or-pepsi.com

First thing that comes to mind when you see or hear these words?

(another word, sentence, or super short story)

Name

1. Corn on the cob . . . .

2. Dark alley . . . .

3. Roller coaster . . . .

4. Pigs in blankets . . . .

5. Hamster . . . .

6. Pink . . . .

7. Glow-in-the-dark . . . .

8. The letter U . . . .

9. Hello Kitty . . . .

10. Face painting . . . .

11. Super star . . . .

12. Bell . . . .

13. Sleeping bag . . . .

14. Hollywood . . . .

15. Rock . . . .

16. Piano . . . .

17. Magazine . . . .

18. Watermelon . . . .

19. Bubbles . . . .

20. Subway . . . .

classic

- ○ Waffle cone
- ○ Sugar cone
- ○ Cup?

- ○ Ice cubes
- ○ Crushed ice?

- ○ TV
- ○ Book?

- ○ Beach
- ○ Mountains?

- ○ Go with the flow
- ○ Stick to a routine?

- ○ Ice cream
- ○ Fro-yo?

Favorite relative?

Best amusement park ride?

Favorite game?

Best book?

CO

last things i painted were my nails

1. Name [   ]

2. Best thing in a spray can? ○ **Whipped Cream** ○ **Cheese Whiz** ○ **Paint**

3. Ever sprayed whipped cream directly in your mouth? ○ Yes ○ No

4. Last thing you painted? _____

5. Last thing you had stuck in your hair? _____

6. ○ Donuts ○ Donut holes

7. Worse T-shirt color? ○ **Orange** ○ **Yellow** ○ **Green**

8. What are you a beginner at? _____

9. What are you an expert at? _____

10. Favorite dip? _____

11. Favorite thing to dip? _____

12. Scarves? ○ Luv 'em ○ Hate 'em, so restricting!

13. I heart _____.

14. _____ is epic.

15. Friend with the coolest family? _____

16. ○ Red velvet cheesecake brownie ○ S'more-stuffed chocolate chip cookie?

17. Fave flave for lipgloss? _____

18. Favorite emoticon? _____

19. ○ Abracadabra ○ Bipiddi-boppidi-boo ○ Expelliarmus?

20. ○ Lemonade ○ Pink Lemonade?

I like movies that make me cry

1. Name _____

2. *Last animated movie you saw?*_____

3. Movies ○ with happy endings ○ that leave you thinking?

4. Sleepovers? ○ Fun! ○ Ugh.

5. ○ French Bulldog ○ Irish Setter ○ Alaskan Husky?

6. **Movies** ○ **at the theater** ○ **at home?**

7. Are you a ○ share-your-umbrella ○ every-girl-for-herself kinda girl?

8. ○ Polo ○ Graphic Tee?

9. **Love to see a** ○ **volcano erupt** ○ **total eclipse of the sun?**

10. What does your hair do on rainy days? _____

11. ○ **Write a great novel** ○ **Travel around the world?**

12. ○ Hike through the woods ○ Stroll through the city?

13. Ever danced the hula? ○ Yes ○ No

14. **Very first song you remember liking?**_____

15. Maple syrup on ○ waffles ○ French toast?

16. Ever fallen backwards in a chair? ○ Yes ○ No

17. **Wear shoes in the house?** ○ **Yes** ○ **Sometimes** ○ **Never**

18. If you get married, will you ○ keep ○ ditch ○ combine your last name(s)?

19. ○ Pack light ○ Certified overpacker?

20. FAVE SONG TO SING ON ROCK BAND OR GUITAR HERO?_____

I'll never get rid of my chucks

1. Name

2. On anyone's bad side right now? ○ Yes ○ No

3. **WORN-OUT ITEM YOU CAN'T PART WITH?** _____

4. ○ Italian ice ○ French vanilla ice cream ○ German chocolate cake?

5. Most unusual animal you've ever fed? _____

6. When things get hard, do you usually ○ give up ○ keep trying?

7. SCHOOL UNIFORMS? ○ FOR IT ○ AGAINST?

8. ○ Sweater ○ Hoodie?

9. One thing you'd like to learn to do well? _____

10. **Pigs are** ○ so cute ○ muddy, stinky, and gross.

11. Wear glitter? ○ Yes, love the sparkle! ○ Nah, too gaudy.

12. Glow sticks? ○ Still fun ○ Ho hum

13. Last thing you do before you turn off the lights? _____

14. Love ○ notes ○ letter ○ potion?

15. ○ Brownie ○ Girl Scout ○ Other _____ ○ None?

16. Favorite Girl Scout cookie? _____

17. Lucky charm or something lucky you wear? ○ No ○ Yes, _____.

18. Ever run a lemonade stand? ○ Yes ○ No

19. Kind of business you'd like to start someday? _____

20. **I would love to be president of** _____.

1. Name ⬭

2. Leopard prints are so ◯ chic ◯ tacky?

3. ◯ Seven dwarves ◯ One fairy godmother?

4. How many tiaras do you own? ⬭

5. Mannequins give you the creeps? ◯ No ◯ Yes

6. Ever been in a corn maze? ◯ Yes ◯ No ◯ Not sure, what is that?

7. Last school project you did? _____

8. British accents sound ◯ so cool ◯ smart ◯ kinda snobby?

9. ◯ Pair of glass slippers ◯ Pumpkin that turns into a carriage?

10. Magic ◯ potion ◯ wand ◯ markers?

11. ◯ Sand between your toes ◯ Out too deep to touch bottom?

12. Bowling? ◯ Ridiculous ◯ Fun ◯ Ridiculously fun!

13. What do you talk about more than anything? _____

14. Would you rather be a ◯ princess ◯ princess' sister?

15. Skinny jeans with ◯ flats ◯ flip-flops ◯ sneakers?

16. Today are you ◯ fairest of them all ◯ "sleepy" beauty?

17. Three words to describe your life? _____

18. Favorite song to sing with friends? _____

19. How 'bout to dance to with friends? _____

20. I wish I were a(n) ◯ English ◯ history ◯ math ◯ science whiz!

coke-or-pepsi.com

Who's
the
worst
of the
fairy
tale
foes?

○ Wicked
queen step-
mother

○ Super
mean
step-
sisters

○ Other

_____

_____

● Coke ● Pepsi?

● Hot dog ● Hamburger?

● Milk ● Dark chocolate?

● Butterflies ● Dragonflies?

● Small talk
● Deep conversation?

● Sneakers ● Flip-flops?

Best movie ever? _____

_____

Worst movie ever? _____

_____

Favorite number? Why? _____

_____

● Reality show ● Sitcom?

● Bicycle through Europe
● African safari?

What scares you? _____

_____

Fave school subject? _____

_____

It's the gotta-have accessory
for every Coke or Pepsi? girl—
the Coke or Pepsi? App
for iTouch, iPhone, and iPad.

Play Coke or Pepsi? alone or with friends.
Answer questions from soul-searching to silly.
Then watch for the release of more
question packs!

Share your answers on the same phone
or Bump to exchange answers. It's the app
that reveals what you and your
friends are really made of!